THE WOMAN TELLS

THE WOMAN TELLS:

Make Believe and Reality Are Only Steps Away from Being Joined. It Makes You Think about Who's the Real Me.

KARLA DAVIS-LUSTER

ISBN: 978-0-578-80983-0

DEDICATION

This novel is dedicated to all the men and women
in successful relationships who have figured out
the formula that works!

TABLE OF CONTENTS

ACKNOWLEDGMENTS

Omar A. Bey	Actor
Dino Clark	Editor
Erin Davis	Public Relations, Social Media, Graphics
Keiten Davis	Graphics
Yashin Daulat	Flower City Productions, Cinematology
Angelo Ellerbee	Double XXposure Media Relations
April Dumas-Grey	Editor-Sneak Peek
LaShonda Hartzol	Editor
Grace Hynes	Cover-Photography
April Jenkins	Cover-Model
Travis Lloyd	Web Design, Graphics, Tech Support
Anita Luster	Editor
Haider Tawakali	Flower City Productions, Cinematology Assistant
James Washington	Maseo Photography
Dan Winston	Print
Lynn Winston	Cover-Graphic Design
Dionne Woodson	Actress

Chapter 1
INTRO TO LIFE'S BULLSHIT

Life is all about what you make it. Goals and dreams can come true. However, you have to be willing to put in the work to see it through. Not every door you try to enter will open. Not every person you encounter will have your best interest at heart (including the person who you commit to). Most people hope and pray that they initially find their soul mate out of the gate, but maybe the day you chose your other half, significant other, or whatever we are calling them these days, you discover later into your relationship that your barometer was broken and you were subjected to a miscalculation of vibes.

As such, I like to think that I am a very intelligent, adventurous woman with a working device. I like to think that my life experiences, interactions, relationships, and friendships have given me great insight into the way people in general think and walk through life. Assessing personalities, vibes, and characteristics, or the lack thereof, has been second nature to me with a keen sense and women's intuition. Every woman has it. Yet sometimes we read things wrong due to our broken barometers. Nevertheless, you must be in tune with yourself and know when and how to use your intuition. Your job is to learn how to distinguish between your intuition, unnecessary jealousy, and an irritable menstrual cycle. Wouldn't that be an accomplishment?

For those of you who have mastered the art of defining which emotional stage you are in at the moment, role-playing should be a cinch. Therefore, this should be an easy read. Which brings me to a tip about this novel. I will discuss, demonstrate, and narrate throughout this journey, conversing about various roles that individuals play in a relationship.

As for those who are still learning the power of your womanhood and guys, your grown behaviors, I pray this framework will help. I pray that you are able to follow where I'm going with it.

I plan to create fictitious relationships that model after real life shit that men and women in a relationship, entanglement, or whatever the fuck it is go through.

Yet again, because I'm not a one-sided person and I try to look at life in a fair way, this will not be a male-bashing extravaganza. Women, we have our shit too. I will talk about several kinds of women and their thought patterns when intertwined with men.

I will also speak on how men look at a situation. How differently they approach it. I plan to create the explanations that men typically use when trying to defend their stance on why a situation happened in the first place and the reactions exemplified by the women involved.

Let's get started. Let's begin with a scenario, "If I were the other woman." So, if I were the other woman, I would think that today is a good day to talk about somebody's man who's taking care of me. The thought of taking a bougie queen's husband, in my mind, would be an accomplishment. Bougie B's walk around like they own the world and are untouchable; on the other hand, as a sidekick, we get that your man may be kicking you down and has it going on, but he also does the same for me. He takes care of me so that I lie low on the side. That's usually a requirement of the sidekick.

As the other woman, I often think that he couldn't really care that much for the woman at home when he's with me most of his free time. As a sidepiece, sometimes I might be in a situation myself. Married, unhappy, lonely, unsatisfied with my surroundings, or just looking for an outlet or an occasional release from my bullshit life. Whatever the situation, I want your man and am trying hard as hell to come up and be you.

My perspective is that "who wouldn't want more out of life?" We see life differently through another lens unlike what you are looking through. The grass is greener on the other side—wealthier, larger, more adventurous, and stable. My, the other woman's, thoughts are, "You shouldn't knock a girl for weighing her options or at least putting up a hell of a fight for some positive change." Well…change. I guess bringing misery to another is never positive, but if it helps to advance status, let the best "B" win. Daily thoughts of a sidepiece. Trust me, I have come to play. I don't think I ever received the girl code that shouts this is a forbidden zone. I don't care. By the time the main woman wakes up or gets from the mall, shopping (something I get to do, as well, on his dime) and not paying attention, your competition is planning to be shopping even more once your man is mentally long gone. Don't leave out that I'm working on the physical to follow.

As the other woman, I habitually am inclined to work from the inside out. By gaining the man's trust and heart. I work at being that perfect woman in his sight. Exciting, attractive, submissive, and fun. He loves what I do and how I do it for him. I will do whatever it takes and will do it well. I will do whatever the main won't. I'm a puzzle, and the mystery keeps him coming back for more. Cinnamon the stripper in the bedroom, Betty Crocker and Martha Stewart in the kitchen, and portraying to be humble and submissive like a First Lady of First Cathedral.

It's just a matter of time before the signs and signals I'm sending the main woman start to show up through her man's sudden lack of interest, absenteeism, inattentiveness, and unavailable behavior, landing my ass in the driver's seat. Keep shopping and acting unaware. I guarantee you that my intentions are to wait, sit back, and enjoy the ride until it's my turn to drive. That's usually the focus. So beware if you are the current blind driver. I'll continue acting out and talking shit in another chapter explaining how I got to be this way.

So let's move to discuss the woman who currently holds the title of the driver. The wife. If this is your chapter and you are driving, unless you wake up and stop swerving off the road, you might crash.

Now let's talk a little about the driver, the main woman, or whatever your title. Simply put, the woman who's being cheated on. You start to feel insecure and rejected by your dude. You start to feel a void. Instead of going to the mall, figuratively speaking, or whatever you are focused on at the time that is causing you to not pay attention, my suggestion is maybe you should start thinking of strategies and taking some time to do things that might help repair whatever's broken in the relationship.

If you are clueless on how to move, sometimes there are books you can read like this one. Steve Harvey has an opinionated one with a perspective. Maybe some pointers from a male friend/boy on relationships might help. My indifferent opinion on where you get your advice is whomever you are comfortable with. Make sure they are going to be honest with you and that they are in a successful relationship themselves and have an unbiased attitude. Make sure it's really a safe zone. Maybe start by seeking counseling, talking to a pastor, or, here's an idea, start with a conversation with your mate to weigh in on just how checked out he or she is. You can use any means necessary to help if this is something you want. However, make sure it is not from some old bitty who's bitter and angry at men. Perhaps your friend who hasn't had a man or couldn't get a man if you, I, and Jesus helped her.

When we are in a difficult situation such as this, realistically we can play our hand better just by being more attentive to what our man is asking for in a woman. "I really hope there is a sale at the mall." Once again, figuratively speaking. We tend to forget whatever it took to get him; a pair of red bottoms and a tight-fitting Herve Leger dress is what you need to keep him. Perhaps you had on a jogging suit with a ponytail. Just make sure you know what he likes. Reinventing the wheel is not always the answer. Some originality will probably be what will keep his attention along with some creativity to recapture his mind. A little thought put into your hairstyle may not hurt if you discover that your man is one for change.

As women we tend to be our own worst enemies. We are very disrespectful, envious, jealous, and unwilling to see another woman happy. In most cases when you are having an issue with your man that involves another woman, the man most likely is not the only one at fault. However, we are so blind and caught up in our own thing that we can't see what is really the issue, i.e., what's causing the problem. Whatever the cause is, when there is another woman at hand, he is typically maneuvering through the two of you like a kid playing his parents against each other when he/ she wants something that they, the parents, differ in opinion on how it should go. In this case the women differ in many ways, or not. Depending on the man, it could be a plethora of women who he's entangled with. He likes something about each one of them. Together they make up his ideal lady.

However, let's take the easy way out and just assume there is only one woman—the fictitious "B" we are speaking of and acting out in this novel. Still too crowded, unless you are into that "superfly triangle" BS, then you should probably stop reading now because this book is going to piss you off. However, stick around and let's flow with it.

He's telling you one thing and her another. Normally the scenario is set up to go like so: He has a "main boo" and the others. The non-mother-fucking-factor bitches are just trying to become relevant. Don't make it easy for them. The main boo is usually the wife, a longtime relationship woman hoping to become the wife, or someone wearing the title until the next top model in his mind comes along.

You know in your heart that things are not right. Your women's intuition is kicking in. We discussed this tool at the beginning. Times and dates are not lining up. Holidays are cut short, with him saying "I need to do this or that," or are non-existent. He starts feeding you that holidays-are-not-important BS. This line could be told to either woman, depending on his feelings and what's going to help his happiness and enjoyment, not taking into consideration the feelings of his woman, whichever one who's on the wrong side of the coin.

At the end of the day, it's all about him. You are just along for the ride and pleasure of your mentally controlling assailant. Maybe I should not use that word because it describes someone abusing you physically. However, in most cases the man really does love his main woman in his own way. Nevertheless, we are not going to make excuses for him and his good side. It's the other guy we are speaking about right now. Mr. Hyde, not Dr. Jekyll. You get the point?

You are constantly feeling empty. Things are not happening that caused you to fall in love in the first place. Once stuff hits the fan, the games have begun. Actually, they probably were at play when you joined the party. Those old, hidden, or well-acted-out habits that drew you in. You

7

read the memo late that he was an asshole. However, when he's with you, that vacancy is still there because something is missing—his mind and attention. He's fulfilling the required checklist to shut you up. You feel as though he's going through the motions to avoid questions and an argument about the state of your relationship. You feel unattractive, lonely, and right at explosive. He's trying to build his case that you are the one at fault.

In the olden days, our mothers felt the pain but kept the peace due to being dependent and trapped. Nowadays a percentage of women are far more combative and willing to move on if pushed. What's love got to do with it?

Of course, circumstances can come into play that cause you to have to consider otherwise. A few things to consider might be the children, finances, etc....However, what can make this even harder is the sidepiece (the other woman) gets beside herself. He loses control of her and the woman tells. Game on! You are willing to fight for what's yours.

Nevertheless, while preparing for the challenge, you go through all kinds of emotions, upsets, and fuck-you moments, even entertaining the thought of leaving. Thus, creating your cross, you become vulnerable and susceptible to your own scenario and potential revenge.

A woman scorned. There is nothing like it. As mentioned, the sidepiece will tell you. Not literally, but she will figure out a way to let you know that she is a significant being in your man's life. Of course, it could all be in her head. But really your man was being just that—a man doing anything to smash. In his mind she is just a pastime that got out of hand and was easy. If her intuition is working, she feels and knows that. But the thought of this bougie B winning is not an option. She continues to try to let you know how important she is to your man. Keep in mind, most times it's not up front where the man can see it. Of course, she wants to remain innocent, down with the cause, his loyal sidekick, and an "I got your back" type of a chick. She's disguised in every way that he thinks is perfect behavior of a woman. Soft-spoken and obedient. Guess what? If you let him know who you suspect as the other woman through any means, he's going to protect her by making you feel like you are crazy, insecure, and starting stuff with an innocent woman. She'll be all kinds of "just cool," "my homegirl for a long time," "harmless," and "not my type." "She's not like that" BS. He will say, "That's your problem. You don't trust me." The oldest line in the history of cheating. "Why are you always questioning me?" "Why is it that you always think that I'm with another woman?" "You must be doing something yourself." "What about that nigga always pushing up on you?" "The only people who think that way are guilty people."

In your mind you are thinking, "Good point, player. You might just speak my revenge into existence." Keep reading—that's the next chapter.

As such, he continues with, "Maybe if you did some of the things a woman is supposed to do like cook, clean, and _____" (fill in the blank for your situation), "you would not be worried about what I'm doing." "You need a hobby or some friends or some different ones." "Your girl just mad because she doesn't have a man." In retrospect, be careful because your girl just might be Becky with the good hair.

A diversion to turn around the conversation concerning the real problem. That scenario might play out in my sequel.

However, men can come up with some interesting defenses when trying to cover their asses. Women, if you sit back and use your intellect, you can come out ahead every time based off the theory that a woman can outsmart a man when it comes to detecting shit. Keep in mind, this theory has not been proven, but it sounds good, so hypothetically let's roll with it. The theory is that men have larger brains than women. Women tend to have higher IQs than men. As such, it takes a man longer to process a thought than it does a woman. A simple fact must travel farther in his mind than that of a woman. Therefore, women think more quickly. So where are we going with this?

Let's look at this in terms of driving somewhere. Back to being the driver. You and your man both start off in the same place. How you both get to your destination does not matter. It's all about who arrives first. Ninety-nine percent of the time, your routes and the way you get there will be different. The end goal is to get there first. Based on this theory, who will get there first? Of course, the woman. The route that he used was from his father's old playbook. Outdated, slow, and full of extra turns. You, as a woman, jumped on the highway, minimal turns, and was there waiting on his ass.

Steve Harvey said, "Think like a man and act like a lady," however this is very contradictory to a female's chemistry, but anything can be learned and mastered. Men are physical, and women are emotional. This is a theory that has been emphasized since the beginning of time. My point is emotions often cause the female gender to act out and express what's happening inside. The downside to that is your opponent, the other woman, has graduated at smothering that behavior (or at least in front of your man).

Generally speaking, most of us have not mastered the skill of protecting our thoughts so that others are not aware of our feelings and moves. We have to learn how to use our emotions to work in our favor. We must model after my corporate sisters, who have been trained in the art of a smile masked with deceit, strategic thinking, and analogies. Thus, not in all cases. Be it happy, depressed, envious, accomplished, challenged, or blessed. Whichever woman you are. Somewhere down the line when we are emotional and out of control, the woman tells.

What's the lesson in this? The lesson is for you to use the information and theories that you know to create the scenario that will cause you to regain control of your life and relationship. Control is just a matter of speech covered in a tactic. You need to use your intellect, looks, and whatever you had that originally attracted him to bring him back around to your team. In some cases, the other woman may possibly have been the other woman before he met you. Maybe, maybe not. If that's the case, apparently he did not see her as his significant other in the first place. If she joined the stable after you, that makes her a filler for the void you caused in him by leaving him unattended.

Everything that is displayed in this book has the possibilities of having one to three sides of the stories, scenarios, or endings that can play out. I chose to speak on this one.

Your job is to knock her off of her kilter and regain his attention. Try to be creative, adventurous, and unpredictable.

Try to think outside of the box, not too far that you become a concern, but become a "God damn" in his eyes. Make him think and say, "I didn't know you had it in you, Baby." Make his ass have a moment on how good you or it is.

If you have never taken a shower with him, surprise him one day and join him. Maybe rent out a room that allows you to cook inside of it. Airbnb for a change of scenery. Hire a chef to start the night off with a candlelight dinner. After dinner is done, have a massage therapist show up. His and hers. Something to relax you. Maybe a nail tech to do his-and-hers manicures and pedicures. Once you are done, change into lingerie he's never seen you in before and in a different style than you normally wear. Maybe even grab a wig. Be "Strawberry" for the night. Remember the other woman is Cinnamon. Thoughts of her is not what you want. Whatever it takes to shock him into saying "wow, Babe" is your ploy. "What's up?" or "What's going on?" are some of the questions you want him asking. "I like the new you."

It's your responsibility to figure out what it will take to get a pulse out of your man. Now within reason. You do have to take your feelings about the other B into consideration as well, but keep in mind the other woman is doing all of this and much more. She has a head start. Keep in mind you won the marathon a long time ago. Time to brush off the track shoes and dust her ass. She's doing research on a daily basis to keep his interest. From lap dance classes to body makeovers. Barbie ain't got shit on her.

What is your man's vice? Is he a church guy, street guy, intellect, geek, baller, or introvert? Meet him on or at his level and find out what makes him tick. Most of all, you have to be more interested in him and his affairs than the woman he has made his temporary concubine. She is really trying to over-take and become that lead driver. She's definitely tired of being a hoe with benefits (unless her situation dictates that's all she can be).

The other woman should never be looked at as competition but as a lesson to stay focused on what's important in your relationship. The lesson in this is that what you have can be taken away if you don't appreciate it. You have to water it like a plant in order for it to grow. You leave it un-watered, it will dry up and die. Treat him like a plant that constantly needs watering. Some plants require watering daily, or it could be one that is less often. Maybe he's a cactus? Old and dry, but at some point, it needs to see some water too.

Watering can be challenging and it could cause some bitterness. You may ask yourself, "Why does everything have to be about him? I put my blood, sweat, and tears into this relationship and all I have received back is loneliness and a side bitch. I feel like I have constantly had to keep it together. I feel very unappreciated and empty. Why should I bother? If you can't appreciate me, someone will."

If I were a lonely woman, I would probably feel like I needed something to make my life meaningful as well. Like I mentioned earlier, this could actually cause a person to behave in another way they said they never would. Make believe and reality are only steps apart from being joined. Like the movie *Us*, it makes you think about who's the real me and what I'm capable of. Situations unamended appropriately could cause the afflicted party to be open to temptation simply caused by a lack of time, consistency, and a lot of other things needed to sustain a healthy relationship. I say a person because it could happen on either side. Keep in mind, your man is not the only one needing to be watered. If this were the case, let's role-play a situation that can happen involving the woman who was unwatered and decided to take a sip of the sparkling water offered her when she was thirsty. Imagine that today is the day the main woman is tempted, and allow your mind to envision it happening just like this.

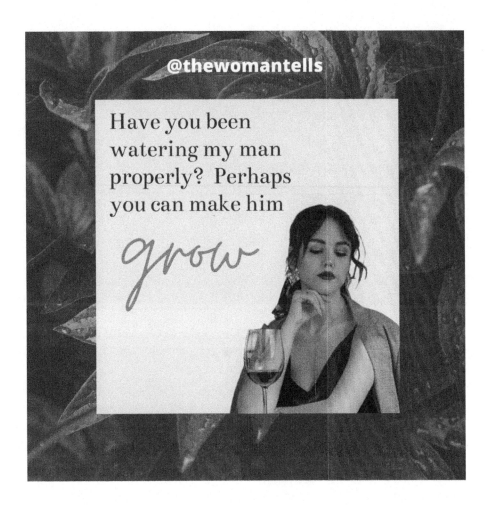

Chapter 2
CAUGHT OFF GUARD:

How did I get Here?

If I were a woman who had it all financially and had children and a dog, but I couldn't get the attention of my husband unless I were his favorite sports team or a fast car, I might be tempted with what's disguised as good.

Let's imagine that life at home had become a challenge and filled with boredom. Leaving room for what's to come. My husband, as mentioned in chapter one, was out most nights entertaining the other woman. I was left to my own thoughts, work, and self-motivation, so much until I was asking myself, "Why should I be the one responsible for keeping the spark in the relationship?" All he did was come home whenever, take over the remote, ask what was for dinner, and crash. He never asked to take me out to dinner anymore or wanted to do anything fun. It was all about what he wanted. If he was not out with the boys (so he said), he was watching sports and very unattentive to me. I didn't feel it necessary to put anything extra into how I looked because he didn't see it anyway. All the shit I bought when at the mall was basically hanging in my closet with tags.

He was overly critical and rude. If I asked him if he liked something, his answer was always "It's OK," or "Aren't you the so-called fashionista." Whether I'm that or not, I was looking for a pulse from him. I was quite aware of my fashion ability and how I looked. Hmm, I guess that response had consistently made me feel some kind of a way. It had only made me think of the women I had seen him look at and admire. He occasionally looked at women, out of the side of his eye, who looked like one of his exes. It made me think and say, "I guess if I were homely with extra-wide hips, flat ass, labeled as a hoe, or short with a stinky female private part, I would have no worries. (You told me you argued about this when you got ready to get busy. You said she blamed it on coffee. You gave it that excuse to feel better about what was *really* going on down there. It made you feel better about your bacteria-infected bitch. Let's call it what it was. Hmm, *coffee was not the cause, bro.*)

You also mentioned that her body had too much surgery. You also spoke about some Russian (or whatever she is) bitch with a flat ass, with *no* body anywhere in sight, a female beer drinker with a witchy vibe, running around calling herself your best friend, your wife without the papers, and her normal.

I'm sorry, readers, I'm jumping ahead. The stinky-private-part bitch and the Russian witch belong to the dude I'm about to talk about. However, *all* of them were *funny looking as hell* in the face. I guess that's the connection between men.

Back to the point. Maybe I would get some respect and play if I had something noticeably off going on. However, being a secure man (so you say) who likes to have a bad bitch on your arms apparently was a straight lie.

Oops, jumping ahead again. Well, beauty is in the eyes of the beholder. Obviously, with the line-up I just described. As a normal woman, I like to think that, being naturally pretty, I may have been too much for you. Having a muted woman who says yes to everything is your thing. A successful, smart, ride-or-die, assertive, and willing-to-be-honest-and-not-just-appease-you woman, who gets more offers than a real estate agent with her looks, is a helpmate who cooks and cleans, can give you feedback (something that you hate to get but love to give), and loves you more than life. "This is what you cannot handle or appreciate".

Your comfort zone has been everyone walking around on eggshells, kissing your ass. Including your woman. I'm willing to kiss your ass, but in another way. However, when you do decide to take me out or go somewhere for our once-in-a-month adventure, I see you looking at other women wearing the same thing you just told me was just OK or you did not like. That's fucked up. You break your neck to compliment other women. When I do something, I have to ask for feedback or your thoughts. Your reply is always, "Oh, you did OK." You're often impressed with what other women do. I work my ass off and balance a million balls while those other women you're complimenting had help from twenty people, and the shit is half-cocked when you read the fine print. Let's be clear—I don't need the feedback to be assured, but it's nice coming from your significant other.

Nevertheless, things have a way of taking a turn. Just showing up without rhyme or reason. I must say, I like what I do. I can't say that I love it, but it beats having to answer to someone and punching someone else's clock.

Coincidence and chance were instrumental in bringing me one of the most joyous episodes of my life. It happened to me without any warning. I guess I'm telling someone's truth—the wife's. I was not looking for it. It took me a moment to realize that it was there. I found myself being drawn into this web of lustful thoughts. I must admit it—every moment inside of this experience had been better than the minutiae I was going through over these past years with my husband.

It was a fall evening; nothing unusual, just an evening. He walked into my existence. That is exactly what it was. I was existing. Not knowing that one strong look could develop into a simple curiosity that would lead to my many firsts.

Floating through time day by day, the friendship began to grow. I was afraid and reluctant to pursue anything other than business, but fate and that animal attraction and connection would not go away. I was infatuated and didn't know it. The daily kind words and compliments began to compound into a blissful anticipation of what could be. Hmm, compliments. However, I have always kept in perspective that all things are usually great in the beginning, uneasy in the middle, and plain ole painful on the way out. But I dare not think about the end because where I am now is better than a pair of Giuseppes, a Louis Vuitton, a Birkin bag, or a Versace gown designed exclusively for me to rock at a red carpet event. "It was so Gucci." Fashion is my vice, so that's saying the most since I spend most of my time at the mall.

Let's park here, at the happy place—the beginning. I like to think that I am a very polished person when it comes to controlling my feelings surrounding a man. However, love has a way of making you act out of character. The cat-and-mouse game had begun. The games went on for a while. Easy prey was not in my résumé. Pre marriage, you had to have a strong work history to get an interview with me. Ninety-nine percent never got a callback. It took my husband a year and a half to even be considered (fill in the blanks).

We finally moved to a place of comfortable communication. I looked forward to the calls, drop-ins, and anything to be in his company. My stomach in knots, while my girl was throbbing and turning flips at the sight of him. I felt sixteen all over again.

Moving backward in time. What could make me defy my beliefs? Although I was feeling the way that I did about my cheating-ass man, my morals, values, and upbringing would not approve of what I am about to describe.

It was a simple look, the right words at the right time, and a little bit of attention that got me. All the things I was needing to be watered. As discussed in an earlier chapter, God knows it was something that had been nonexistent. "Thou shalt not commit a sin" was the upbringing, but sometimes it has a way of creeping in and taking a seat, getting you to participate before you can say no.

Religiously speaking, I would say if you were rooted in the word, this would not be possible. I like to think that

"For all have sinned and fallen." "We fall down, but we get up" is the rebuttal to that debate. When caught up, at this point you don't know what's right from wrong. Well, the right thing to do in a dope circumstance. What a web we weave. A lot of times we are forced into situations due to a lack of feeling important. Once again, as discussed earlier, let's not give excuses. The same rule applies here, ladies—back to let's roll with it. Let's do just that.

When you have been a victim of trying to please for a long time and eating the favorite dish that someone else liked, and now, suddenly, that stops and the table appears to be set with the menu you prefer, it sparks a different mindset. Living another's dream inadvertently caused me to forget about my own identity. I made another's happiness more important than my own.

Thank God when we go to sleep, we eventually and hopefully wake up. Sometimes the time zone we awake in isn't the one we were in before lying down. In this case, I woke up in bed in a scenario that has kept me happy and smiling. At least for a while it did. In the beginning, I woke up in tune with what felt good and was not necessarily the cookie-cutter white-picket-fence blueprint.

"Only by falling in love with the unusual, or shall I say someone unusual, could I be this open, literally." Vulnerability is a MF. This had me thinking totally differently moving forward. Hmm, I was actually thinking about me. How I looked when I left the house in the morning. Not needing a stamp of approval or a stamp of approval from home.

It had gotten me prioritizing. What did I need to accomplish? I was thinking about how I was going to do things and how I would accomplish the task. What was plan B, C, and D? I was currently living in plan A, and it did not seem to be put together in my favor. These exciting thoughts were rekindled. I have always been a boss. I lost my way in another's dream. It was so refreshing to be back to loving me. My new, special sin situation running through my mind all day and most of all some excitement to look forward to was just an additive. I am a person driven by what's to come, who I'm doing it with, and the actions moving us to the finish line. That was the dream and time zone this new journey took me to. Once again, stay tuned because we could run into some repeated behaviors seen in different characters.

Back to the unexpected situation. The cat-and-mouse phase of my new boo chasing me and my playing hard to get. Over time he wore me down to a point I wanted him just as much as he wanted me. It was not hard. My other half had his thing. The other woman was trying to be me. She was trying hard to take over my comfort zone. So why not? I guess for the moment I had elected not to water the cactus.

The first time we went there was kind of quick. I think there was so much anticipation and emotions built up, it was a wonder he didn't just release in his pants. We began to spend as much time together as we could spare. We were "boo'd up." I found that my heart had moved from one spot to the other. I took the bait.

Reminiscing on one of our encounters, we spent an afternoon and evening together. Our experience from the tub to the bed lasted about four hours. The woman tells. I showed up to his place one afternoon, thinking we were going to talk and have some lunch. To my surprise he had prepared what you would call a "lover's lane" setup. He started off by preparing a nice tub with bubbles and rose petals. Very sensual. There were candles all around, champagne, and a hard pole waiting on me. He gently helped me out of my clothing and escorted me into the den of love. Water is always connected with shrinkage. Apparently, he had discovered a cure because that never came into play. Conversation to indulging to conversation. Hmm, it's better left for the imagination. I'll allow you to get some mind exercise.

I will talk a little about another encounter that happened that almost made me call home to say, "Baby, I'm never coming home." I had found my male version of Sunshine like in the movie *Harlem Nights*. Not that I would be missed or that he would answer, considering he was probably out with his hoe.

Driving in his 64 on a nice evening, top down, music bumping, and he was looking like a cup of my favorite Italian ice; you can imagine him to be whatever flavor that causes you to say it was worth the calories. His hand was up my dress touching my girl—or shall I say, my happy place—my head was back, and he was occasionally looking at me to see if I'd reached heaven. He was talking to me, telling me to let go. The faster he drove, the closer I got there. Finally, in an isolated area, he pulled over. He wanted to participate. He got me there. Back to beginnings is great. The leather seats were very hot, like the passion we shared. I had never met a better kisser. He looked at me while making love. It was very isolating. Meaning it was off in a place where no one had taken me. I say lovemaking because what I felt could not have been anything else but love. I know many would question if lovemaking was really what we were doing in this story, but the actions and the commitment I had seen, pulling me onto his team, and his telling me constantly that he was in love with me had me trusting that it was true. I needed to keep it in perspective to prevent me from being his first. The first girl to hurt the ultimate catch. I was not looking to hurt him but keep him.

That statement could mean several things. I was something different to him because he did not have me totally. In his mind he only had me in the sexual and mental state. Challenges were his specialty, but this one could turn out to be the whopper. Stay tuned—more to come. He tells his version in chapter 6.

Well, I thought this love experience was so exciting. Maybe the mystery of sneaking around, the anxiety of what the next time would be like, would I see him today or tomorrow, would he wake up in another time zone with someone else or move on were all thoughts and built-up anticipation. I have to assume that I'm not the first. He's full of, "You are so beautiful," "I want you," and "I can't wait to see you." All moves in the beginning. Gifts, dinners, movies, trips, and flowers. When we were out, we were the center of attention. I guess that happens when you have two people who are both bosses, both unusually attractive, confident, dressed without flaw, and having fun. Who would not want to be in that company?

The beginning. Keep in mind that old saying, familiarity breeds contempt. What I liked most about him was the way he moved and how respected and respectful he was with everyone. As I looked at him, on occasion you could see darkness behind his eyes. I could not quite put my finger on what it stemmed from. Was he married with lots of children? Was he a man with a woman on every corner? Did he really love me, or was I just another conquest? I say conquest because he had revealed that losing was not an option for him. If I were him, depending on how important this experience was for him, I would be looking to make it a permanent thing or another milestone to reach to add to my greatness and accomplishments. What would life look like if I were to become his final ploy or conquest to make me his wife? What a scenario that could become.

According to what we share and how compatible we were, life looked amazing. Adventure would be second nature, thinking back on another wonderful sex-spent evening in this relationship. I can remember meeting him at a club to have dinner and taking in some music. I was not aware that he happened to be an exclusive member at this club with special perks and offerings. The high-roller pleasure amenities.

I got there first. I had no expectations or thoughts about how the evening should flow. I made sure to look my best, as usual. A sexy dress, heels, nice bag, and makeup to perfection.

Waiting anxiously, I was entertained by admirers, stares, and compliments. The funniest comment that I received while waiting was from this gentleman who walked up and asked my name. Of course, I was reluctant, but what's the harm in sharing your made-up name? LOL! Well, his line was, "I thought your name may have been Google because you are everything that I've been searching for." I chuckled and thought he read that somewhere, practiced using it, and went for it.

Nevertheless, I was still waiting on what would turn out to be a very seductive evening. Suddenly the hostess walked over to me and said, "Can I escort you to your room now?" My first reaction was, "What room? I'm sorry, I'm here for dinner. I'm meeting someone." The waitress proceeded to say, "Your host has arrived and asked me to escort you up to your private quarters." My ego shot up to 110, and now I knew I was in love.

We got on an elevator that took us up to a floor with a member-only-permitted-beyond-this-point sign posted. We finally arrived at the floor we were going to. There were lots of very bougie, rich-looking individuals socializing, partying, and partaking in drinking, smoking cigars, and enjoying foods like sushi, shrimp, and numerous selections of finger foods for the upper tier. I noticed that there were several bars, various sections (like a Vegas club with seating for different parties that you pay thousands of dollars to have with bottle service for a few hours), a dance floor, and the usual you see in a club. What was unique was that there were enclosed private suites or rooms if you wanted to be isolated and out of view from others. Without question, one of those suites was where I was escorted to find my love waiting with food already ordered, two champagne glasses, and soft music playing just in that room with its own controls and dim lights. I think I stopped breathing.

He was dressed very casually and sexily with a suit jacket. Shaved, smelling amazing, and smiling with one of the most beautiful smiles I have seen on a man. I thought that I would never say this, but Idris had nothing on him that day. He greeted me with a hug and kiss. Our evening began.

We talked and listened to music, he sang to me out of tune but adorably, and then it began. He put his hands on my face and pulled me close so that we could kiss. It was on from there. Before I knew it, his hands were up my dress and fingering the shit out of me until I saw stars. He definitely was not going to allow me to enjoy it all alone. As I remember, I was holding on to the door of the exit to prevent any of the waitresses from walking in to check on us. He entered me from behind, and the rest was history. He is a guy who thinks about everything. He had a change of underwear already there for me, to my surprise, clean-up material, and something to take care of our breath. Funny, but it's reality.

I found myself so struck until I was concerned. This guy was way too perfect. It was as if he had truly gone to charm school for how to win a woman over. No other man stood a chance against him if it were someone or something he wanted. A master at winning a woman's affection.

Wow, I felt as though I were going to need counseling because we all know that nothing good lasts forever, and what was to happen? Was I a fling or whatever the end of the story turns out to be? I felt that I would not be OK. Thinking back on chapter one, was I any better than her, the other woman? Was my excuse for how I got here valid? Was this a lifestyle for a dude or his vice, wooing women until he was done with them? Or had he met his match, and I had been placed in his life for some retribution for past weak bitches that he ran over, and they didn't measure up, according to him.

Keep in mind, I wasn't an easy prey to begin with, and for the record, fast men—fine, rich, and you can finish however you like—have come at me all my life. The majority was part of that 99.9% crew I talked about. I might be starstruck for a second, but turning around a situation has always been my specialty in any situation. So what will the future hold for me? Because the woman will tell.

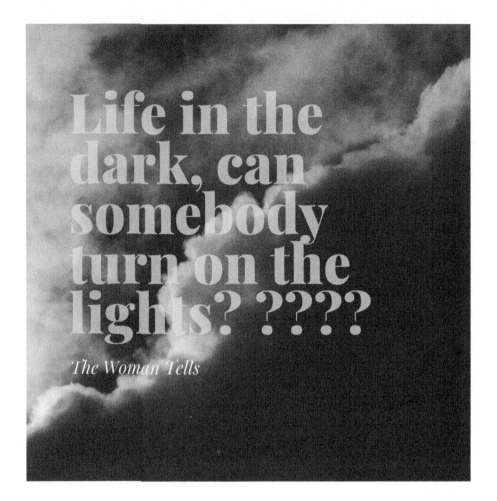

Life in the dark, can somebody turn on the lights? ????

The Woman Tells

Chapter 3
CONTINUED SINFUL BLISS

Well, I decided to allow you to indulge in this scenario a little longer. One more blood-warming experience was an evening spent on his yacht.

I showed up thinking we were going to spend time talking and enjoying the weather with a nice glass of champagne, some junk food, and some interesting conversation due to what had transpired. We needed to talk about a misunderstanding. Hmm, we were moving toward the middle.

When I arrived, he was there looking debonair as usual. He smelled like a billion dollars, and of course his behavior was that of a Wall Street broker who had just closed another deal. Arrogant, confident, and in control. This is what he did and did it well.

We ate the dinner, or shall I say, junk food. Shortly after, we began to talk about our issue. He had this way of making you feel like the point you were trying to make was totally incompetent, silly, and really was your fault. The conversation was full of his saying, "That is not the way it went. You are making things more complicated than they have to be." He told me that he does not like confrontation, and if there were anything important he felt I should know, he had no problems sharing it.

He asked if we could pick this up later because a couple of his friends showed up. To be specific, we were out with some of his friends. He had started to bring me around his inner circle. He was a very private person. So in my mind I must have met the "move forward—she's special" approval. The night was going so well. The circles he moved in were very coed. Everyone happily enjoying themselves, talking shit, and making the best of a great thing.

Of course, there's always one glitch to mess up your night. A want-to-be-important motherfucker who won't shut up, or an annoying, leeching bastard showing up empty-handed but wants everything, or a bitch who's hoping to become significant in your man's space. Well, can he be called your man? Can you guess which one kicked off that evening?

Anyway, the one I zeroed in on, of course, was the want-to-be-significant B. I noticed that her girlfriend she had with her was acting very shady and unfriendly toward me. You always know what's up in a posse by the weakest link in the group who can't hold it together enough to play something off. Nothing, of course, the male gender or your so-called man would recognize to be strange.

Let's take it back to what we learned in an earlier chapter. We discussed how to utilize your women's intuition. Yes, the vibe was present. To confirm that she was on some other shit, she was all over my Prince Charming. It was obvious that she was accustomed to doing this and was accepted, because he did not budge. He was looking at me like there was nothing wrong.

The other woman can come in many forms. This one, I think, in layman's terms was the "groupie." She probably had screwed more than one of males in his circle. Overly friendly, dressed like somebody's pilgrim, and looking like a knock-off Storm from the *X-Men* about the head. Yes, she had old-fashioned platinum hair. Some tacky mess from the eighties. Well I'm not sure of the decade. Pick one—it doesn't matter.

Funny, because in chapter one I was describing the other woman connected with my spouse. Remember I also jumped ahead describing women attached to this guy, my new lover and Prince Charming. Is this an epidemic? Is it an accepted rule for which I forgot to read the memo *again*? This should not be happening with my extracurricular activity. You were supposed to be my happiness, not adding to my stress and acting like this female's behavior was OK. All I needed was for him to start defending her. Oh my God! I was in the middle, and if this shit kept up, we'll get to the end real soon. I guess the question was, was he any better than what I had?

Needless to say, I started to feel some kind of way. Finally, my guy noticed and asked what was wrong. Of course, the woman will tell. I shared that I was not a fan of her behavior and I felt disrespected on his part because it was his place to stop it. I shouldn't have to. He pretended that he did not know what the fuck I was talking about. He said that I was tripping on an innocent woman who's been with and around his posse for years. That was not what she was on, and I was causing problems. Hmm, does this sound anything like what I've already spoken about in an earlier chapter?

Well, as we continued throughout the evening, I think this bittie had gotten wind that I was irritated. Now, the other woman was really telling and letting me know that secretly I was right about what I suspected. She was significant, and I could get ready for a third party because she was here to stay. She was here before you, so get with the program.

Well, what the fuck is a girl to do? In my mind, I was imagining; I was acting out in my head all of the characters, scenarios, times, behaviors, and events. I imagined that I snapped off and beat her motherfucking ass. (Oops, I kind of went off-script.) I was a lady, and that's why we are now having this conversation about our issue on his yacht. He tried changing the subject by being affectionate. It worked. End of conversation but not the issue. His friends had left earlier, including the groupie.

We stayed longer on the yacht after his company left. While he was seducing me, we began to kiss and touch. Intimacy was never our issue. The feeling was that of real intensity due to the emotions built up from conversation, his making you feel like you were his world, and what could possibly have been wrong along with touching in the right places to build the mood.

Before I knew it, we were in one of the cabin rooms making love. I was in another place that I had not been emotionally again. I probably needed to call a corporate sister for more advice because emotions just kept getting the best of me. Well-endowed, he was thrusting harder than usual, talking to me, pouring his heart out with words any woman would want to hear. It was like he was making up and punishing me all at the same time. Controlling me and making me forget about my issue. We were in love.

Well, this lasted a while. He picked me up, and suddenly I was holding on to the edge of the bed in the second room of the yacht. Remember, we started in the first one. He was behind me making me answer questions. "Who does my girl belong to?" He continued to ask them while we were in the middle. He told me that I was his "B" forever. He continued to murmur how much he loved me, how good my girl was and that he never wanted me to leave him. The encounter continued on the stairs and back up to the sitting area of the yacht where we began. Hell, we christened the entire inside. All I saw was beige, Veuve Clicquot, our bear with Burberry that we called our son, and designer bedding. We kept him on the yacht in the summer. One funny—while in one of the rooms, he bumped his head on the ceiling the way it was made. Not for a big guy; the main quarters were more comfortable. It was a hell of an evening with not one of my questions answered.

This man had made love not only to my body but my mind. I'm not sure which I preferred. His tampering with my thoughts or when he inserted. He not only made love to me physically; he mentally made me forget about the other stuff that I was upset about.

He had a way of turning things around, calming the mood back to the way he was comfortable with and then asking me to do something that made me feel like I was 100 % the apple of his eye and affection. He was either in love for real or a master at BS. I had access to all of his amenities.

He constantly tried to make me feel like he was totally dedicated emotionally and physically faithful. He always stated that he had a lot of female friends but it meant nothing. I would always ask what was different about me. He would state that the difference was that they wanted him but he wanted me. His line was he loved me to pieces. It made me think. Could this motherfucker be a serial killer? He often choked and slapped me passionately during sex, or is he taking some script from *Fifty Shades of Grey*?

I'm reminiscing on one last encounter that I'll share, or have you fantasized enough? Not only did we experience intimacy but the fun was off the chain. He called one day and asked if I were afraid of heights. Of course, not wanting to admit that I'm a punk, I said no. He asked me to meet him at a spot, park, and he would pick me up. We drove to what appeared to be some kind of private airport. He had rented a private jet. We flew to the Keys and took a ferry to a private island where you can rent sections out for hours, days, or whatever your pocket could pay for. We spent the afternoon on a private island, drinking fruity beverages, being massaged, and jet skiing. He had all I needed already there waiting on me, including a hut to shower and to complete the day making love. We finished the day eating a seafood dinner.

He was definitely an experience. That is exactly what he would call himself—an experience. However, anybody this adventurous has an attention span of a toddler. You get where I'm going?

As time passed, I, on occasions, started to observe how his eyes could sweep a room. Hmm, those wandering eyes.

Almost like he was looking over merchandise at a department store. There were lots of brands and designers. Typically, you had your go-to favorites. Sometimes something new caught your eye because it was different, it made a statement, and you had to have it. Now as I think back, I think I fit that description the day he first saw me. Different. Not a groupie, not easily impressed and desperate. He always said that he liked bosses, someone who was not looking, a challenge, and untouchable. The forbidden fruit, good girl, mature and older with a young wit, stable, sexy, attractive, well-spoken, and accomplished. Belonging to another was quite the chase in itself. Or…at least by title. I think after spending time conversing and sharing, he knew there was a loophole of loneliness and a void needing to be filled. I started to think that women were a collector's item to him. Like the shoes and clothing that he wore. Like various items still in packaging in his place. It was not a debate whether or not he liked nice things and liked his lifestyle. Settling down was still out for a jury to decide. Had I met my happiness and demise all in one?

Being in the middle, you would suspect that talking about anything would be OK to speak about because you were comfortable with each other and no question should be taboo. He tended to get upset when certain things were asked.

He had shared early on that he was seeing someone when we initially started talking. Was I in the twilight zone, or are they making clones and men are ordering the same model? He described her like one of the females I described in the earlier chapter. What's with the fucking coffee? Women, female hygiene is a must. He said that their relationship had run its course and that I had moved in and pushed her aside.

Well, if you are thinking like me, it sounded like a bunch of bullshit. Every time we were together, his phone rang. I knew it was Alice. That's what I will name her. He only picked up on certain calls. He talked about how she was going crazy when he left her. He said she told him that she was going to fight for their relationship. Well buckle up, bitch. The only way you will get him back is if I release him to you because I'm done or dead. Hmm, I'm acting like the other woman. LOL! *Crazy.*

He called her lazy and said he had helped her get back on her feet. He was constantly looking at his phone for text messages and certain phone calls. The person would keep calling every couple of minutes like a desperate person. If that was not behavior or sounded like a woman who was upset and desperately trying to reach her man who kept disappearing. You are not reading this book. You are asleep and dreaming.

Keeping everything in perspective, I had someone at home as well. Was there really an argument? Did I have a right to complain or judge? Was there a reason for him to be lying? The real question was, was he really into you and willing to go the distance? Or maybe you just picked up the same scenario that caused you to be open to this little shindig in the first place. Just food for thought. Was it worth the aggravation to be headed up the same river? Should you have traded one for another? Was one better than the other or just different with the same ending? At the end of the day, how did you feel, and what was actually making you happy? Did you even know what happiness is and what it takes to be happy? There were a lot of ways this could play out on both sides. We have statistics that we can take a look at:

This information is based on various studies conducted by a number of magazines and associations not named in this book.

- Women who entertain extracurricular activity: 45-50%

- Men who entertain extracurricular activity: 50-60%

- Divorce caused by infidelity: 20-40%

- More than one affair: 42%

- Finding out about the affairs, people who said that they would leave: 62%

- "I will stick it out": 31%

- Noted by one magazine, 70% of relationships that experience infidelity actually stay together.

- Men who cheat who divorce their wives for the other women, according to the divorce magazine, is actually a very low percentage: 3%.

- Of the 3% who divorce their wife, 75% of those relationships end in divorce as well.

- Women, in every case, were the ones who were more prone to initiate the divorces.

- The number of women who cheat who divorce their husbands is a higher percentage than that of a man, according to the relationship experts.

- Women are more apt to make a decision.

- According to womensinfidelity.com, 70-75% of women initiate divorce.

- The percentage of male paramours is about as high as mistresses for men.

How does Webster define some of the terms that we are using, such as *paramour* or *mistress*, and what are the differences?

A paramour is a lover, often a secret one who you are not married to. So it's best not to kiss and make eyes at your paramour in public unless you want to be the center of a lot of gossip. This term evolved from the French phrase *par amour*, meaning passionately or with desire.

A mistress is primarily referred to as the female lover of a man who is married to another woman; in the case of an unmarried man, it is usually to speak of a girlfriend or partner.

At the end of the day, your scenario and what happens at the end of your scenario varies. It's all up to the individuals who have a role and your situation. What we tolerate is all based on our own personal feelings, character, beliefs, and decision making.

You will have to keep reading to find out how this story ends. The conclusion might show up in novel two or three. Who knows? However, keep in mind that there are more than one scripts that can be played out. Everyone involved has their own perspective. Including the other woman or man.

However, back to this one. He continued to say how in love he was and how he wanted to spend the rest of his life with me. I was only my husband's by paper; everything else belonged to him. It was just a matter of time before I belonged to him totally.

We continued to gallivant, but he occasionally started to disappear and become scarce. The romance began to get spaced out. He started to ask questions about what I did at home. "Does he touch you?" Yet at certain times and moments he was the invisible man. If asked, he always turned it around to be that I was being negative and that I was worrying about the wrong stuff.

Here's the kicker—one day while on social media, who do I see but Mr. Private himself posted up with a Russian witch-looking chick trying to look fly. Men, what's with the weird-looking bitches? This was the one I described in an earlier chapter. He had spoken about her negatively before. Can I get a beer? Let's keep it classy. Let me ask, "Is this sounding like some entanglement repeat bullshit?" Was that my Prince Charming who had given me full access hugged up with a wannabe? Let me guess—his best friend? Here's the funny: when I asked him about it, he went off and said she had posted *old* photos, and she's crazy and was trying to make an old boyfriend jealous.

You have to give him credit. It was original, but how third grade. I guess he forgot she was wearing his hat in one of the photos while driving in his truck. He had just bought a group of them. He showed me the hats in several colors, and they had animals that were noticeable as hell. She was wearing the black one with the bear on it. Guess what? The very next time at his place, the hats were still on the counter, and the black one was missing. Hilarious player!

We named Alice, so let's name the Russian witch for future reference. Let's call her "Due-key" with off-white frosting. I tell you, dude, not even a rapist in a creepy van would want this one. You missed the boat on the bad bitch standard you thought you had. He probably met her on Myspace.

Chapter 4.

FUCK IT, IS THIS THE END?

OK, we were familiar, and we had boo'd a while. I'd gained five pounds from the dinners, endured all the great love-making, and agreed to the menu for each day with Dude. Predictable as usual, the way relationships trend, he sprang on me that his hours at work were starting to pick up. He was totally focused on a project he wanted to complete without a distraction. Do you hear me, ladies? Now I have moved to being a distraction. After almost five years in. Yes, five.

He told me to call him, and he would let me know if he were available to *probably* go to dinner only on Thursday because he had a work trip over the weekend on some business he had to handle. I asked where he was going. *Houston.* Can I get a hoot, hoot! The answer was vague. The conversation surrounding the trip turned out very questionably—not to go into details. Can somebody tell me where those flowers were that went along with that weekday dinner?

It was apparent his feelings were strong. He put in the time to prove it. I definitely was not a fly-by-night or one-night stand. Nonetheless, I think I was one of several choices he was trying to decide on. He was a man of goals, and the woman on his arm had to fit.

We have now landed on the downslope. Here comes the bullshit. Actually, it was probably already happening the minute I met him, but I was too vulnerable and starry-eyed to see it. I found myself calling and not getting an answer. It used to be that he picked right up or at least texted me to say, "I'll call you back in a minute." He still appeared to have interest, but it was not as strong as the beginning. He was familiar, and it was no longer new. I was in love and contemplating. He was in love and deciding. He had made moves with me that he'd done for no other. He was used to being treated like a king and first. I could tell my having to go home to another had taken a toll on him and had caused him to shift his energy in a different direction. Like I said, the middle was uneasy. Analyzing behaviors, less joy at the fact that he used to eat, sleep, and breathe my company. Now he was thinking, "I can see her when I can. She's cool, but I'm not really feeling her that way right now because she can't fully commit. I love her to pieces, but at the end of the day, I have to keep it about me. I'll get up with ole girl a little later."

He was starting to become more absent. We were still getting together. Still rubbing skin. It was less passionate and started to feel more like he was with me, but his mind had wandered into another time zone. When we were together, what he really saw and thought was starting to come out in conversation. His frustration was showing what he feels. He couldn't have me 100%.

I asked him, "Can we go to dinner?" and he said, "Maybe we should do something that involves cardio." Remember, I was content and had put on five. Now he was noticing my flaws and pointing them out. Keep in mind, my eyes were clear now too, and Idris still had the throne.

Our conversations had slightly changed. Not as guarded and nice. More to the point and matter-of-fact. I wanted to believe everything he said, but actions and words were starting to not line up. He was still charming and able to keep me wanting more, but that female intuition was telling me he had allowed other stuff to occupy his attention. His competitive, jealous streak had started to appear. He was criticizing everything. He also said, "I know, at the end of the day, you don't need a nigga. Bitches out here are weak. You must have a bit of testosterone. When you find a woman like you, you hold on."

As a woman, I was unsure at this stage and started to seek others' opinions about my situation. I was giving my version of the scenario, leaving out pertinent information that was bad. Hoping that they told me what I wanted to hear. Not the truth, however, and the truth is what I needed to hear.

Get my car in gear. Drive the fuck away or park my shit on another street. I would say home, but we still need to complete that story. How about I drive to a garage and park? Here's a thought: with this repeat-behavior MF, drive down a street called Use-Your-Common-Sense Lane. Deep down inside, I know that here it comes. I was hoping; I was antsy. I was no longer his first thought or move, but I had taken a back seat to other things or person(s). Still, in his mind he got to you when he could. The middle moving to the end was uneasy, like I said.

Keep in mind that your female still ran through his mind because she had been good to him. In the beginning I had a wonder hole. I was so tight, he thought I was a virgin. Fresh, barely touched, smart, and easy on the eyes.

He loved the fact that I was a boss myself, like him. He often said we could be a power couple. He liked that I didn't bond easily with everyone. He felt exclusive.

But…with his gradual distancing, in reality I started trying to not think about him as much either. I was starting to try to do things that took my mind off of him. In retrospect his behavior had become somewhat dismissive and abrupt. What happened was that I did not take the advice of my wise surroundings, shouting out clues when they clearly told me how to handle this situation. I let my heart and emotions drive me down Heartbreak Boulevard. I went back to the mall. While driving, I should have played it smart and turned down a street called I-Got-Your-Number-My-Player Avenue. I clearly knew what was best for me.

First of all, I should have made a decision regarding plan A and completed the process before I started anything else. Maybe the cactus should have gotten watered or could still have been watered. Was it too late to take my throne back now that I saw that I could not trade one dictatorship for another? As such, I blindly did for a moment.

I found myself in another game that I was on the same page as my partner. Wrong! My prince was playing chess, and I was playing checkers. Checkmate—he just was not into me as much anymore.

Maybe I should have listened when he started to be controlling with his conversation and repeatedly said that he'd never not had his own. Two things were going on: he felt himself getting too involved, felt a dead end, and wanted to beat me to the punch in his mind, or his intentions were not as he initially portrayed. Both roads appeared to be heading toward disappointment. Really? What exactly was I expecting out of this scenario? Well, the thrill was leaving. The newness was wearing off.

He had probably found my replacement and had her start the program to see if she would graduate and assume my position as the driver. Hmm, does this sound or look familiar? This ending could be downright painful. As a woman, it was so hard to know that I was not the one he was looking forward to being with. Another had taken his attention or never lost it. Was it possible that he had the same thing going on at home and was in a relationship, and his woman took a different route and decided to recapture what she had? She left the mall and went home and watered the shit out of her plant? If that's the case, from experience, he was not a cactus. So not only had she started watering often but she also had to add some plant food.

Absence was too hard to swallow. The best thing was to keep busy and try to find other things that interested me and occupy my mind. Assuming, thinking, trying to figure out what was going on, what I thought, and maybe this was what was happening. All of that energy to figure out what was going on would keep me in a very dark, negative place that could cause me a lot of stress.

Once again, maybe I should have watered the cactus. Maybe it was not a cactus at all as well. The other woman appeared to be keeping it moist. Or maybe both were not right options, and I just needed to stay parked until I figured myself out.

Time after time I have watched family, friends, and many people go through the stages of a relationship that had gone astray and somehow had managed to work it out to be happy, no matter how dysfunctional, but worked for that couple. I have also seen people leave for the other one and be happy as hell they made the move.

Surprisingly enough each party in the relationship has a self-motivated agenda. Be it pleasure, companionship, a stress reliever, time waster, true love, or a game. Each person comes in with an expectation. When I hear people saying that, "I have no expectations for the relationship," "I want it to just flow," "I enjoy our time without pressure," I still look at that as your having an expectation. It's just without labels or constraints on the relationship. However, that's still an expectation. It's just not the usual talked about or the typical.

The problems will still come into play when feelings start to evolve for one and not the other. You start to not be on the same page and now are expecting two different outcomes. Updates and check-ins are necessary. People change. Be clear and precise; that way there are no surprises. Keep it above board. Of course, we are all human and can change our minds due to some unexpected inserts that happen, such as falling for someone unexpectedly.

Obviously, this brings me back to this case. Neither of us expected for this to go this far. This became apparent in this situation. Feelings shifted in an already destructive relationship that was built wrong out of the gate. Which brand of shit was best? I could not get mad at the fact that he'd started to fade and was not willing to go with what was said and established because he wanted more. I took him somewhere he had not been.

So, let me ask this question: who was really in the wrong spot? Twist and turns. Him or her? Her or him? Both were in love. The difference was that she was operating out of emotions, and he was trying to protect his heart that she had stolen like a thief in the night. Hmm! However, as an upfront adult, I would hope that both were mature enough to state their poison and move on. But if by chance you are caught up in between, you have some decisions to make. You need to decide if you are going to give it a timeline, hoping for change and your expected outcome, or just move on.

Advice for both scenarios: Purgatory is the wrong place to be inside your heart. Neither party can be upset because feelings stayed the same for one and changed for the other party. They decided if what was best is to do something different or not. Maybe you are not as compatible as you thought. Or maybe you really are soul mates. Could it be timing? The waiting game is necessary. Good things come to those who wait. No more or no less.

You might want to ask some questions about your extracurricular activity investor—both sides. Have they had other relationships? How did they work out? Is there a pattern of relationship changes every so many months, years, etc.? Should you take it further or become serious? Are there children involved? Did they tell you about them? What are their ages, and how involved are they with them? If you are like me, they should be involved and doing everything a parent should be doing. Brings me to how responsible are they? Where and what role does the baby mama/daddy play? The problem will come when and if they are still involved with the person and the baby mama/daddy still wants them. Children are sometimes used as pawns to manipulate situations, causing major problems within a relationship. *Run!*

Back to the storytelling. He called and wanted to finally talk.

A perfect day would be that your person feels the same way that you do, and you both graduate in feelings and expectations. Now you are working with something. But don't jump the gun too fast. Let the next stage play itself out. Have your conversation at every stage to keep the communication flowing. Because I have always been told when you assume, you can make an ass out of yourself. I'm one that likes to know and be told what's up. Even if it's not what I want to hear. With that information it allows me the opportunity to choose if I want to be a part or not.

Always be prepared for what could be or not be the outcome you anticipated. Get to know the person, their ways, their pet peeves, what they truly like to do. Not the things they agree to do at the beginning of the relationship, trying to please and impress you. You might want to let your hair down as well to ensure you and your person are not doing what I call the "rehearsed behavior." It's not just men who do this. I spend a lot of time observing people, not just one gender. You will find that a lot of women create this perfect person to appease men as well. I mentioned this about the other woman.

I have to tell you about one more scenario with my Prince Charming, or the other man. One evening we were back on the yacht with some more people. I think they were his boys who brought friends aboard. A group of thots who I did not know and a couple of family members.

To get to the point, one of the thots came on the yacht with an agenda. Of course, coming straight at Mr. Wonderful himself. Instead of sitting up top with the rest of her crew, she decided that she was cold. Coldhearted is what I say, but that got her a seat inside the cabin with family, me, and, of course, my pleasure.

So, the woman began to tell. She began to talk about how she and her boyfriend were having issues and that she was tired of him. One word lead to another, and soon she was in full force talking about how well she took care of him physically. Graphically describing how well she thought she would suck him off. She said that her game was tight and she was the best. Of course, she was attractive, thick like guys like them, nice hair, and full of game that seemed to be attracting the opposite sex who were listening. He played it off very smoothly.

Before leaving, she left her number with one of his boys. Knowing, in her mind, that it would make it to the right person. Interesting. This game kept going round and round. How can I get mad when all the time I am there under some other pretenses myself?

What do you think happened? More issues and arguing. I'll let him finish this story in his chapter. We calmed down. We made love, but this was kind of different. I started cramping really badly and decided to call it a night. He asked if I wanted to lie down some more, and I replied no. I just really needed to go. He walked me to my car. On my way driving to the house, the cramps got so bad I drove to the emergency room.

THE WOMAN TELLS

Who is that creeping in my window? I don't care, my alarm is on.

Chapter 5.

RUDE AWAKENING

After the trauma I experienced in the emergency room, my mind continued to ponder over our situation. I thought, What the hell? Are we on the way out or making a decision to stay? Will he move on to the next adventure?

As discussed briefly earlier, while driving, did I happen to notice what route he took? Did I not read the street sign? It was my stop. Your Uber ride had ended. I ordered the XL size, but my emotions and pride could only handle the economy size. What time zone was I in? Maybe the same one, but it was possible he woke up somewhere else. The end or the same one as you.

Well for now, if I'm right, a good woman is hard to find. In some cases, your partner is able to realize that and do a complete 180 back to what's considered home. But the question is will you be there or available? Will it be the same and as fun as it was or different? Do you want to possibly do a repeat of another messed-up situation? Or was the situation to your satisfaction?

He's probably thinking through the same questions. I know it hurts to let go. Sometimes that is your beginning of happiness by cutting the stress and clearing the path for something beautiful to happen. What's meant to be will be. Should you part and it's meant to be, it will come full circle back and without stress; it will be sanctioned and both parties feel good about it. However, most women keep calling, texting, trying to go places to hopefully run into him, and all of the above.

Back to learning to control your emotions. Keep in mind, this love affair was not biblical in the first place. "How did I get here?" you constantly ask yourself. Unhappy, open, and reaching for fulfillment? My husband failed to see the signs that I needed more and wanted more out of the relationship. He was too busy being someone else's Prince Charming, paying attention to the other woman, and left me to fend for myself. I guess if I asked him, he would paint a completely different picture of why the relationship was going sideways. Let's imagine my husband's perspective right now. It could go several different ways like the other scenarios, but let's have his start off like this:

I remember the first day I saw you. I thought I had died and gone to heaven. God had blessed me with a girlfriend, BFF, stripper bitch, and wife. Someone to match my intellect and mother. I liked the fact that I had my bad bitch all in one. I had someone that I loved being seen with. We could walk into any establishment and command the room. Men looking and imagining. Women watching and hoping. Conversation would go on for hours, filled with intelligent perspectives, facts, and debates that got me thinking and wondering if my answer was the right one. That's hard to do with someone like me, an arrogant prick who has been used to everyone agreeing with him all the time, not truthfully, but sucking up because of who I am. She was a woman who could challenge or intrigue my thoughts. Of course, I'm that MF that knows everything about every subject.

Moving on to what's extremely important to a man—the physical. The sex was off the meters. At least for me. Tight, untouched, not overused, clean, and ready to receive what I'm packing. Connecting on every level. The things that we did are not to be repeated. Talking about it only would send a nigga into cardiac arrest. Best way to go.

She was different, I said to myself. She's unrestricted. I, on the other hand, was restricted to what's comfortable. Now I had found what or who would cause me to be un-restricted to what's possible. She was the possible. I knew she was with me not because of how others saw me but as a person.

Most of the time what's comfortable is the thing that you are familiar with or it with you. I was always told familiar-ity builds contempt and is boring as hell. The meaning of contempt is the disregard for something that should be taken into account. A person's preferences, likes and dislikes. What scared me were my options. Picking the wrong one and find-ing out the one I chose had contempt in their heart. Acting as though my needs were of the utmost importance, but all the time, only there for what they could get or an easy ride.

My wife, on the other hand, was close to perfect for me and always took into account what pleased me. The shit I liked and the shit that drew me initially. So let's talk about that.

Originally, I would come home to a clean house, a home-cooked meal, and a woman who was happy to see me come through the door. She bore me several children. She would smell good, Prada Candy perfume. She often changed it up. It most definitely smelled better than what my sidepiece wore. I think some bullshit by Estee Lauder—Beautiful. Loud, old fashioned, and annoying. However, lingerie on point, hair bouncing, makeup to perfection. What else could a man ask for coming home from a long day of dealing with the streets? *No* nagging, no complaining. Bath water ready with some nice oils and beads, candles, a bottle of Cristal, and chocolate-covered strawberries. Soft music. My happy stick got waxed without asking and with no instructions needed. She was willing to do and deliver whatever I asked. Thoughts of me were second nature to her, like walking and breathing. She cherished her man and was concerned with my happiness.

Nothing she asked for was too much because when a man loves a woman, he will go to the end of the world expressing it and protecting its sacredness. What I mean by sacredness is ensuring her of her place in my life without any question. Always taking care of her needs, emotionally, physically, and financially. If going to the mall makes you happy, then off with my black card you go. I made sure that your living quarters were comfortable and dope, you drove the ride of your choice and the maintenance you like, mani-pedis, facials, and regular massages and spa days were often.

All this happens when I am made to feel like the king of my castle. So what if I was out often, traveling, attending my social shit I like and whatever else I wanted to do? What woman would start to shut down because she felt that I was not committed and failed to do her duties? Yeah, I said duties. I'd watered her ass enough. When you are a man, shit happens. Especially when you leave us unattended because you feeling some kind of a way about shit that does not matter. Or at least initially, in my eyes. Let's talk about that.

She got upset about a situation that occurred when we were at an event. We attend a lot of events. The woman was married, there with her husband, and not totally my type, for crying out loud. She was only doing a bit of innocent flirting.

It started when my lady and I were sitting in an aisleway across from each other, participating in a game at a couples' event. It was a game night event. The young lady that my girl claimed was disrespectful was one of the event hosts. Her and her husband. What kicked it off was when the host squeezed her ass through the middle of where my girl and I were sitting. There was only a small space in between us, and instead of walking around, the lady walked through us, having to step over us. I will not admit it, but the shit was foul. She fanned past us, damn near putting all of her ass in my face when she clearly could have simply walked around. Like most men, I acted oblivious to what was actually happening. She clearly was fucking with my girl and flirting with me all at the same time. My girl was two minutes from snatching a knot in her ass, but instead, she maintained her composure.

Women were always coming for my girl. She set a standard that not many could live up to. This woman continued to do small things to let me know that she was interested in having something. She always played it off around her husband but did not give a fuck when my girl was around. It became sort of a thing. Deep down you could tell she was jealous of my girl but had a thing for me. She almost seemed like she could become a fatal attraction.

However, me being me, I knew I could hit it because she had just as much to lose as I did. Just as long as no one took the shit out of perspective. From my understanding and rumors, this bitch had stepped out on her man several times. He was some goofy MF running around trying to be important while his girl was hoeing it up.

She was fairly attractive by the body because of her wide hips (or maybe because she wore her clothes super tight) and tree-trunk legs (you could tell this by a couple of occasions when she wore a short dress). It's not a compliment but would work because they were big and not shapely at all. The tight dress made up for or camouflaged the fact that she had a flat chest like a boy and flat ass, which has always been a turn off. She had decent hair, but somebody a man would fuck. Facially was not pretty enough to be called Mrs. My wife would always call her funny looking. We laughed about it on occasions. I know that's being a hypocrite, seeing that I was smashing her, but the shit was actually true. And to make my girl feel better and to throw her off, I would actually point out things about her myself. Personally, I think it was her matronly look and aura that indirectly attracted me.

It sounds warped, but I discovered within myself that she was no challenge or threat. Men looked at this woman but not like they did my wife. Her attention-getting was all generated by her approach and open willingness to go. My wife's attention-getting was effortless and unsolicited. She probably was intimidating to a lot of men. Once again, it was not like someone who would ever be my main woman. She already had an idiot.

On another tip, I actually felt a bit bad for ole boy because this bitch was secretly aggressive. She often showed up to various functions and would make eyes and stare across the room when my girl was present. The issue I was having was that my girl was smart as fuck and doesn't miss shit. She had a radar for female bullshit, and on the other hand, this woman did not care as long as her husband was not around.

Another scenario was when we were out at another event with a lot of people; my side hoe and her husband were there. She and I had been kicking it on the side for a bit, breaking away on occasions to have lunch, smash, and whatever we could do within the time we had before either of us were missed. We would have drinks, laugh, screw, and talk. We had a drink that both of us liked to order when together—a strawberry daiquiri.

The night was young and in full swing. We both ordered a strawberry daiquiri while sitting with our significant others, secretly acknowledging what we shared by having that drink in front of us and knowing in our minds what it meant. She was a lot of fun. However, she could not touch my girl in any way, yet, as men we lose perspective when "p" is involved.

I often said that if something came up regarding that woman, my wife would be livid because she knew the situation surrounding this seemed off. My girl was very secure in herself and was not intimidated by women. As such, I think this one being so disrespectful caused the disturbance. No more or no less. My wife was used to me being around model types. As she puts it, why would I single out a half-cocked misfit?

My extracurricular pastime went on for a while. Things at home were starting to change. What I mean by that is my girl was starting to act differently. My girl stopped complaining, stopped asking where I was, and stopped doing her duties. She started to be absent herself and quiet. I don't like quiet. When women voice their opinion, it lets you know what they are thinking and feeling. As a man, that's easy to manage. It lets us know how to move. The silence was a different move for her and me. I wondered what the fuck she was up to.

I no longer needed to create an unnecessary argument to leave hostile, acting as though I were furious. She was beating me to the punch. Those nights I had reserved for my side girl, saying that I was going to play poker, were reluctantly in the clear. I found myself not enjoying the side's company and thinking about what I had at home and where she was. I used to smell the chicken walking up to the door. All I had to do was come in, and she took it from there. Short of fanning me and feeding me grapes, she would start fixing my plate and wait on me.

Be careful what you ask for. You just might get it. I prayed for her to be quiet. I was not liking this feeling—as though

I were not the center of her life anymore. She really acted like she could take me or leave me now. Yet, I also asked to get next to this other one. The more I looked at her and the more time passed, I realized that there are not a lot of woman like my wife, my girl, and my world. I really hoped that my arrogance, inattentiveness, and lack of presence had not driven her into something that I don't even want to think about.

I did notice at one event there was a gentleman there she knew and was very friendly with. There were lots of men who found my wife attractive, including some of my closest friends who I had been around for years. They made comments. They teased me, which caused me to stick my chest out because I knew my wife was fine.

Hell, when I met her, I couldn't keep my eyes off of her. My wife had a nice body, beautiful personality, and was smart, an entrepreneur, and a great mom. Women admired her or hated her, and men wanted to hang around her with a fantasy to probably fuck her, and she had never given me the notion that any of that meant something.

But for some strange reason, he bothered me. The conversation between the two was overboard. He was exceptionally polite to me, and he had this bad woman on his arm who appeared to not intrigue him as much as my wife's conversation. The woman on his arm was fine but not taking anything away from my wife. The cat was out of the bag. The woman opened her mouth to try to join the conversation, and all was explained. She didn't quite measure up in the intellect department. She was clearly not his match. His soul mate may have been standing next to me. Where did he come from? However, I was not going to spend a lot of time trying to figure it out. At least not in front of him.

Very confident MF. He was dressed OK in designer shit and appeared to be very intelligent. Just what I knew she liked. What bothered me the most was that they matched. Not he and his date, but he and my wife. Of course, it was a coincidence. I could see how someone could walk up and mix up who was with whom.

While his date was in the middle of one of her stupid-ass sentences, my wife got pulled away by one of her friends, grabbing her away to show her something. The date continued to talk to him and me. His eyes followed my wife's ass to the other side of the room. Once again, a lot of men watch her. Why did this one kind of rub me the wrong way? I don't know, but I had a few questions. Hmm, was I starting to switch roles with my wife?

Lo and behold, my side hoe and her husband walked in. This night was starting to be a real trip. The minute she could get away from her husband, she headed in my direction to start some shit. Surprisingly enough, my wife paid her no attention. I don't even think she knew she had come in. She was working the room and taking names. The gentleman and date appeared to have left. My wife was the happiest ever.

The deejay started to play some soft music, so I asked my wife to dance. The side was pissed. You could see it all over her face. But I didn't care. I was focused on my wife and this change she seemed to have.

I love her, but what was in question was how she had begun to feel about me. I'd put her through a lot without any compassion for her feelings. It had been all about me and my pleasure. There had been others besides the side chick. Which this one was starting to irritate me and becoming more and more aggressive. Aggressive women have always turned me off. What I liked about my wife was that she made me chase her. She never came off as desperate and seeking. I know she liked me for me because of her behavior. She had a hard time opening up in the beginning, but we worked through it.

Hmm, the lights had just come on. It was time to go home. The car ride home was silent. She was asleep, and my mind was replaying the night while driving. My curiosity would not let me rest, so I asked her or, shall I say, I made a comment to indirectly bring up the night when we got home.

I started the conversation off with, "You seemed to be mentally preoccupied entertaining ole boy." She replied, "Which one?" Her playing with my intelligence was not a good move for my mentality. It kind of pissed me off because she was very in tune with vibes, actions, and moods. I knew she immediately knew which situation I was referring to. I guess now she was acting oblivious. She was acting like a guy. She must have read that book. It was as if she were trying to fuck with me because I had never paid attention to whom she interacted with at events. I was always nowhere to be found, engaging in my own affairs.

The argument started. Before I knew it, her smooth role reversal with words, demeanor, and comeback had me walking away with my arms folded like Eddie Murphy in *Boomerang* when Robin Givens runs a touchdown for women. Anyone who saw the movie knows that toward the end, the role reversed back, but it's nice like the Democrats and Republicans to control the House.

The night was something to think about. My lady was putting something on my mind. This was not my idea of keeping me excited and intrigued. If this is what women feel when we are doing our thing and fucking up, it's not pretty. Of course, she had not actually done anything but change her behavior and how she reacted to my moves. This new conduct was actually a turn on? She always kept herself up; not sure if she lost weight or gained somewhere, but whatever it was had me wanting to do things to her.

Still, I was mad and confused about all of this. I was supposed to go out of town this week, but I thought I would hang around and spend some time with her. It got tricky when I told her and she said that she would not be around and that she had made other plans. Now I was feeling some kind of a way. My questions were rapidly growing. We would have to talk soon because this change was not something that was helping the relationship.

The more I think about it, my wife tried. I don't like the fact that she got too comfortable shopping and not paying attention to my needs. I guess a simple sit-down would have sufficed rather than trying to fill a void with another person. However, sometimes relationships run their course and cannot be mended. One of you arrives at that point before the other. It's always a sad thing to be at a spot alone. You land in another time zone outside the one your significant other is in. I assumed we would have to do something, because our spirits were not lining up. I guessed I had something to think about.

It's very apparent that a situation can turn around in the direction of the one's favor or, shall I say, we start to drive again when we start to use our intuition, looks, intellect, or whatever mechanism the right way as stated in an earlier chapter. Men, for the most part, are able to flow and run through relationships, flings, affairs, or whatever the title without getting attached emotionally in most cases. But when they do grow some skin in the game or cupid shoots the arrow up their ass, they typically are not built to take the shit they dish out for woman to swallow.

Oh, but what a web we weave when we make it to the edge and manage not to go over. When we figure out a way to climb down off of the mountain into the sunset. What a glorious day when Stella gets her groove back. Watching men try to get down off the mountain is interesting. They take another approach. Sometimes it can result in violence, depending on their personality.

Stay tuned to watch this scenario come full circle. The end could go any way we imagine. Keep in mind, whatever way we imagine it, somewhere in the world it happened for real.

Truth or Dare, both have consequences – and I plead the fifth.

@thewomantells

Chapter 6.

ABOUT THE OTHER MAN: WHERE DID HE COME FROM?

If I were the other guy or, shall I say, the one who took over the heart of the lonely, I would make sure that in some roundabout way, without effort I would piss her man off. My natural presence and genuine commitment to stealing a heart is a God-given talent. My very existence was usually too much for a MF messing up, knowing that he was not standing up for his woman.

That was what I usually did. I assumed the position of caring, loving, paying attention, and all of the above. Whatever it took to have my way. I would think that I was all that and a bag of gold. Yes, many may call me the devil in disguise, a male home-wrecker, or a French term called a paramour that you learned about in an earlier chapter.

However, looking in from another side, people might say that I was a knight in shining armor or a Prince Charming saving her from that life of misery, not being appreciated for the queen that she actually was. You can pick a side after you read the book. But in actuality, I'm human with feelings too. Just looking for something or someone that's great. I was the ultimate bachelor that many women would do anything to get. Minimally a conversation.

I'm 6'4", about 260 lb, and muscular—not overdone but right. I dress for women and what they like to see. I'm fair-skinned with great dimples. My imprint is probably the first thing women see when I walk in a room. I'm very polished in corporate behavior, but you better believe that I'm straight from the streets with respect. My debonair conduct is not an act but comes naturally. I have a voice that makes women fall in love just with a conversation. That usually makes everything else quite easy. I like to surround myself with trusted friends and that special person I keep close when necessary. Opportunities with women come free to me. Ten cents a dozen, in my case, it's free. Meaning most attractive men with their shit together probably have women coming at them a dime a dozen, however my action probably quadruples that. And like I said, my freight is free. Women knowingly share me. Some may call this arrogant and sick. I call it just being in demand, good stock, and confident.

You would think I had many women, sex many times in a day, and a lot of kids running around. Well, I do have children from past relationships but not what you would think for a man of my caliber and opportunities offered to me by the opposite sex. I am a man with standards, believe it or not.

I like a high-quality woman—very classy. Weaves are acceptable on occasions, but I have to know that what's under it could basically do the same thing as the horse hair. She has to have something going for herself, dress nicely, like the finer things in life, and a personality that can roll in any circle, including with my street posse. I do not like to be questioned, and confrontations should be close to none. I realize any two people are going to disagree somewhere in life, but making it a day-to-day episode will not work for me. I like it easy and spontaneous. Not planned and not hard. I'm OCD like a MF. I like things neat and in order all around me from my cars (might I add, I have a fleet), my spots, and anything I'm dealing with. My woman must be in order. Coffee pussy is a problem for me. Believe it or not, I like to keep it simple, non-demanding, and adventurous. Women tend to always want me more than I want them—if I really want them. Most of the time they choose me, and depending on the package, I say yea or nay. Very rarely do I choose someone.

I love fun and belonging to the upper tier. I like fine champagne, cigars, and a fancy lifestyle. The woman I'm entertaining has to be able to move in my circle without flaw. Well-spoken and can hold her own. The most important thing is that she is someone who's well-kept and has not given herself to every "Harry" that smiled at her and called her cute. I'm a man, so of course a thot is good for a night, a bugaboo or stripper is good for private sessions, and my hype girl and friends are used as needed and for whatever event, sport, or situation I need them for when I'm moving around. I'm offered all kinds of activities. Dinners, concerts, and a movie, on occasion treated by the opposite sex, is fine by me. Nevertheless, as you can see, I'm not an easy read or catch due to how over-the-top I am. Like I said, I never really have to choose because it's usually dropped in my lap. But taking some words from chapter two, sometimes things have a way of just showing up without cause.

As I remember it, the first encounter, I walked into her existence to discover a real live "Bitch" that looked like she needed some good dick. Literally! She acted like she had not been fucked appropriately in years, and she was taking it out on her surroundings. She greeted me rudely and with distaste. I was skeptical to even speak to her. I had to because she was checking people in at an event. At a glance, she looked at me with what I call some bedroom eyes, hidden under the deceptive behavior of a witch. You could see that she thought that I was some nigga who was a womanizer or a married jerk who would cheat on his wife. Hmm, that women's intuition.

The interaction was for about two minutes, but interestingly enough, thoughts of her lingered long after the first chaos of a greeting. My thoughts when I left her were that I was going to fuck her and leave her on her doorstep. My first impression of her looks was she was not an ugly girl, but she did not put much into her appearance. Body was nice from what I could see and intelligence was still out for a jury to judge because of the unacceptable behavior. At least when I first met her.

As time went on, the conversation did lighten up, and she was not as wound up as the initial introduction. It was funny because I could see how she watched me from afar. We both belonged to the same social organization. I guess she was new. She initially looked like she couldn't care less about being there and did not care about what others thought about how she looked. Women would approach me trying to get some play. She would just watch and try to act like she was not paying attention.

This went on for about a year or two. The organization only had events occasionally, so we did not see each other often. However, often enough to start minor communication at the events and subtle stares.

It finally happened when we were given an opportunity to actually embrace each other. She was speaking with one of the organization's other members and hugged him to say hello and greeted him with such grace. I saw an opening, and I took it. I invited myself to intercept their conversation and ask for a hug as well since she appeared to be passing them out. Surprisingly she did not refuse. When we embraced, it was like a program was downloaded with all of the codes to make us feel and know that there was something there. It was only for a minute, but it left us both curious.

Time moved on, and the organization was having a major event that would allow me to discover the angel in a dress that she was. God is good, most say all the time; I said I know he was this time. When I saw her, my breath was taken away. She showed up with several friends to whom I paid no attention. *God damn*! She had on this form-fitting black dress, showing her nice, round ass and mouth-watering half-watermelon-sized breasts with some stilettos. After she walked past, leaving her scent, Jo Malone's Mimosa, I knew her shoes were red bottoms.

Over time, I had moved to a place that I really don't go. I wanted to get to know this lady. My original thoughts of fucking her into oblivion, due to her initial behavior, and leaving her had gone. Yet, I still wanted to fuck her. I was interested. That's hard to do. I guess what they say about men is true. They like a challenge. This was a storm. Not easy, she was very intelligent, beautiful, and polished. As it turns out, she was very well-groomed and could dress her ass off. Can we say "label hoe?"

Let me say that we were either related or kindred spirits. She appeared to have come into some happiness that made her demeanor desirable. That bitch vibe had disappeared somewhere in the shadows. Well, she was a bitch but just not mine yet. The "G" bitch-girl thing kind of became attractive. She didn't fuck with everybody. Exclusivity. I loved it. It was on.

We exchanged numbers. I began to text her. Sometimes she responded and sometimes not. This was not something I was used to. Women fell at my feet. This one apparently could take me or leave me.

Through minimal conversation with someone that knew of her, I found out that she was married. To my surprise she was also older. As I watched and looked at her, this bitch was actually finer than a glass of your most expensive champagne. I love champagne. She was not easily broken and influenced. I thought I was falling in love or I may have found the female me.

As you read her version of our love affair in her chapter, I think the way it happened from a male's perspective went a little differently. It was a fall evening when we met; no one can mess up that time of year. As she quoted, most things are great in the beginning, uneasy in the middle, and plain ole painful on the way out. I like to think of any experience as a lesson, and whether or not it's good, bad, or indifferent depends on if you actually gain or lose something. Was your life fulfilled at that time, and did you learn something? Did you gain a wonderful friend and ally you can call when you need to? Not every situation ends in matrimony. If it does, great. But for the time, life was great, so move on.

However, in this case I agree that feelings had come into play. I got caught up and also fell in love. Believe it or not, I was not afraid to tell her. I knew I could not treat her like the other girls. Expressing feelings and letting my guard down had not been part of my vocabulary and playbook. I think I got taken back to my teen years as well. Cool and still in control but young thoughts and a lot of stiff moments. I think I had blue balls a couple of times. Something that happened only in my teen years. Definitely the night I first saw her dressed up. This was something that could possibly get my player card revoked. I had to keep what it was into perspective.

I found myself wanting to be with this woman probably as much as she wanted to be with me. Being the man who I am, I had to pull back and think about the situation. She was not a single woman who I could have my way with. She was someone who could actually hurt me for the first time. It had never been done. However, I was open and free. Being with her made me feel uneasy and caused me to behave in a manner that eliminated my usual self.

As fate would have it, I had met what could actually be my soul mate, partner, and a woman who could measure up to all the requirements of possibly becoming my Mrs. Wow, did I just say that? Personality, looks, business, spirituality, and family oriented. Of course, later flaws would arise, but nothing major that I couldn't work with. At the end of the day, nobody's perfect *except* me.

Just recalling the first time I was able to release was dope. I hoped she didn't hold it against me that I got there kind of quickly. But the shit was so next level, my player ass couldn't hold it after years of practicing not being *that* guy.

Man, that shit was so good I planned another encounter very quickly because I wanted her to experience the real me. I thought it would be cool to invite her over to my place. My place was always kept exclusive. I had women who I had fucked with for years who could not begin to give an address for where I live. I like my privacy, so that's not something offered up. I usually meet them at their spot or my thot hideout and call it a day. However, this one had become special. I found myself wanting to treat her differently.

What I admired about her is that she, in her subtle way, demanded respect and attention. Not desperate to have a man. From what I could see, men came as easy to her as women did to me. Keeping in mind that none of that mattered. She was married, but with the spiritual connection, I felt she belonged to me. Regardless of her status, married or single, as complicated as it was, she would never be alone if not wanted.

Getting back to the day I planned out, she came over to my spot. When she walked in, my dude immediately started jumping out of the gym. He went to ten. Her presence had a way of making my dude act a fool. I think it was her pheromones. She smiled like a million bucks.

Everyone who knows me knows that I love money. Probably more than sex. So when she walked in and sat, I wanted to test how honest she was. I had been clipped in my past. I laid a stack of money on the counter. I would check it later to see if any was missing.

I popped some champagne and had a nice tub of bubble bath going with candles and the nine yards. Soft music that would help her out of her panties. Lights dim, and to complete the puzzle, I was the missing piece. Nice cologne, shirt off, showing my large chest and nice, protective arms. Tall, handsome, and a hard dick welcomed her in the door. She was a lucky woman because my dude stood up in the water. I fucked her for about three or four hours. We started out in the tub. To end the night, we got a bite to eat. I figured I should let her go home to regroup. Her shit was all over her head. It was a nice evening.

By the way, all of the money was there. Here's a twist: it was plus twenty dollars. I loved this woman. The message was that she would not take from me. She would only enhance what I had. She had her own. She did not need my shit. You pick what the message was.

We had many encounters that left me wanting more of this young lady. I found myself wanting her more and more. It wasn't just about sex with her. I wanted a future with her. I love a challenge, and that's exactly what this one was.

Chatting with some of my boys—men do talk on occasions. Maybe not as detailed and informative as a woman, but we can get a point across to our boy. We are used to sticking and moving, keeping a couple of regulars, a hype bugaboo, and flyby friends that fill gaps. Where was I going to put this one? I already had someone that I considered my lady. I found myself in conversations with my lady telling me she's feeling a void. Where in the fuck had I let my heart wander? Complicated was the word. She was beautiful and most definitely wife material. Both. What was a man to do? Was I ready, or did I start the backup plan, literally? Back the fuck up. I was not sure if I was ready to let my lifestyle go. I just needed her to start what men call the "relationship deactivator behavior." Act stupid and turn me off. She actually had a couple of episodes, but rather than admitting it, I am a man, so I turned the shit around to make me the victim. Reverse psychology is a motherfucker. I grew up learning and writing the playbook. None of which made me want to stop seeing this woman.

She had captured my thoughts over the many. Over my lady. This brings me to the most challenging portion; this was an affair. Happy or not, I found myself wondering how far this would go. Would she leave her man if I asked her to? What's up?

We continued to make whoopee and have fun encounters and a continued friendship. I was not sure where this was going. I had tried to back off of her, but I thought I was caught up as well. I loved her, and I told her often. I'm very affectionate. I'm not one of those men who doesn't pay attention to my woman. I complimented her often. I told her when I liked an outfit or her hair, and I loved tongue kissing her. It was very sensual between us. I wanted to be with her, and she knew it. I would just wait and see.

Back to the beginning of my chapter. Many may say I was wrong for pursuing her, but I look at it like this: if the motherfucker would have been doing his job, I would not have been able to move in and steal her heart in the first place. You see, I was not afraid to let her shine and treat her like a queen. She's not Hazel the cleaning lady just cooking and cleaning and tolerating my shit. "Support" is my middle name. If she shone, I shone. If she was my lady, like Jay-Z and Beyoncé, we complemented each other. We were the shit together in a lot of areas.

It pissed me off not being able to wake up to her. I was willing to let go of my stable and become monogamous. I did have some business ties with a few, but I was sure something could be worked out. I tried not to think about the fact that she went home to that MF. I couldn't bring myself to think about if he touched her. I was caught up. Maybe he would get it together, but you best believe, once I set my mind to something, I usually succeeded. The question is, what was my mindset on? Forward or reverse? You can fill in the blanks any way you would like.

In the meantime, I planned to keep living and enjoying what made me happy. Until I decided or something dictated what was going to happen, I was going to play my position. Well, I did have a situation with this other female that I was waiting on results. I liked her a little, but my heart was set on ole girl. Less work, better model, I didn't have to work as hard to get her up to my standards, and most importantly, I was in love. I know it sounds a bit arrogant, but stay tuned. Me and ole girl had been having a few issues with some things I didn't feel really mattered. Woman tend to see it differently.

On a couple of occasions, we had some weirdness. Once on the yacht, she claimed I had started to disappear and become unavailable, but from where I sat, I didn't owe any explanation because she was attached. This was getting a bit old when I could have had just about anyone I wanted. Yeah, I was back to seeing friends and my old standby, and that situation came back to be a positive result. I really didn't know how to tell her, but on another note, I needed to be there.

The situation started when a buddy of mine brought a couple of thots on my yacht. My girl was there with a couple of family members and some friends. I thought the night was cool, but you could tell my girl was not feeling one of the young ladies who was talking a bunch of trash about her man. Apparently, she had an issue with him. She was a very attractive young lady. I think my girl knew she was feeling the hell out of a brother.

Hey, at the end of the day, I was single. I was committed to what we had, but in my mind, until she was 100%, if ever, I was single. In my mind she did not belong to me. At least that's how I had begun to feel. I felt like I needed to start pursuing or rejuvenating others. Of course, she would always be my first choice. But not always that's what's up. No one can totally measure up. If I could turn back the hands of time, she would be Mrs. with all of my puppies. I often said that to her when we were making love. We did it all—fucked, sex, and made love. I needed to be open. I was caught up as much as she was.

Well, back to the young lady, the thot; it turned out that she left her number with my buddy to give to me. So I hit her up to hang out. She most definitely was with it. Turns out that she wasn't bad company. I got to experience those skills she so meticulously described on the yacht. It was good but not my girl. You are comparing it to love. No comparison at all. Just good. Different flavor. Yet I wouldn't kick her out of my bed. You get the picture. This went on all summer. My girl was probably feeling a void. I guess it's a pattern.

Another episode, one night I was with the thot and let my guard down. I got drunk and did not prepare for rain. I needed to figure out how to tell my girl about that positive result. Maybe I wouldn't. She had her own shit. A future with her, I was guessing, was a fifty-fifty shot. I thought I would play all of my hands until it worked in my favor. I had about four months until the addition. Hey, shit happens. My seed is not shit and deserved a chance. I'm a boss. I'm good enough to keep all. Whoever fell off, then that's what it was.

But overall, I was in love with ole girl, and what in the fuck was I going to do? I had to think realistically. I still had my old standby who I had practically left for the queen I was in love with. She would do anything to have me back. Including finance some shit to lock me in. It's not like I needed her. Lot's to think about and work out. For now, I was going to chill and hope for the best.

In the meantime, I thought, Let me call her and let her know that she's been on my heart. We had another argument. I also needed to see how she was doing. She had been very emotional since back over the summer when she got sick and had to leave. I think she was embarrassed because her time of the month happened while we were in the middle. She thought I was mad. A little, but I loved her, and shit happens.

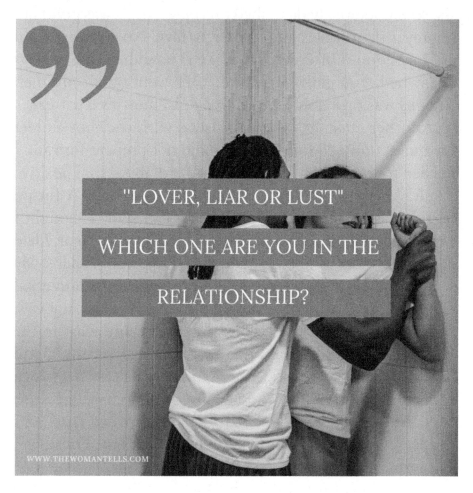

"LOVER, LIAR OR LUST" WHICH ONE ARE YOU IN THE RELATIONSHIP?

WWW.THEWOMANTELLS.COM

Chapter 7.

WHAT PART DID YOU PLAY?

I guess you see now just how all sides can get caught up in something that can jeopardize or even end a relationship that once was happy. Dipping can create an entirely different person. Usually, when either party is unhappy, this can cause them to become a very vulnerable person entertaining another who looked, walked, talked, and smelled good. Spat all the right words that you needed to hear at the time. If things were bad at home or wherever between the two who were supposed to be committed, you got caught up in being mad and didn't realize all that did was cause division. At the end of the day, things you did with the side should have been done to excite the one who actually did belong to you. You felt the guiltiest and start saying you thought you loved him/her, and all you needed to do was make them look at you like they once did.

Thinking about the scenario, maybe it wasn't love. Let's insert a twist that the person you committed adultery with actually turned out to be your soul mate. You never made it to the painful ending, and it worked out for you and them despite the odds of affairs ending. You turned it into a Johnny Cash and June Carter moment. Nothing should have been able to creep in in the first place if both partners were doing what they could to make sure the other one was happy and satisfied instead of pursuing their own agenda of pleasure. Religiously speaking, as the ending would go, never let sin take you off your kilter. All the energy you put into getting back at and enticing a new person, spend that time figuring out what would make your shit work.

You need to fix yourself before you can ever be good for another. Like Tyler Perry so eloquently described in his movie *Why Did I Get Married?*, you may trade eighty for twenty. To elaborate on the theory, how would you even know what that looks like if you are not 100% confident in yourself and know yourself? You have to take account-ability for the role you played to contribute to whatever the outcome may be. Why your partner actually abandoned your relationship in the first place. I'm sure that the other person they hooked up with percentagewise was not all that and most likely couldn't even compare to the attributes and qualities your significant other had. The ones that initially attracted you to their life. Well, maybe, maybe not. These days trading up is the shot. Hmm!

You have to ask yourself some questions, both parties. Where did I go wrong? What street did you turn down to kick the shit off, women? Did you say, "I don't feel like cook-ing"? Was your first date a candlelit seven-course meal that you cooked for him? Were you dressed in a red dress and stilettos and no underwear? Men, did you start off paying her attention and supporting her and suddenly stopped? Women, before the affair and years into the marriage, did you become known for gym shoes, sweats, and a dirty, two-day-worn T-shirt with your hair in a ponytail? Like a lot of older women, did you cut it all off because it was easy? When he met you, your hair was draping down your back, or at least the pack you bought was. Men, before your affair, did you take her places? Did you guard the sacredness like you promised or make her feel secure? These are some questions you can ask yourself while trying to figure out what your next move is.

Once again, both sides. Will you stay and work on the relationship? Will you leave to start over with another? Will you go into purgatory until you figure some shit out? Time, lots of thought and consideration, wine, prayer...At the end of the day, do and be with who makes you happy. Nothing worth anything comes easy.

> "
>
> ## What's yours is ours and what's mine is theirs
>
> THE WOMAN TELLS

Chapter 8.

ABOUT THE OTHER WOMAN: I'M NOT A HOME-WRECKER— OPPORTUNIST, MAYBE?

You were introduced to me in chapter one, and comments have been made about me throughout this novel. But now it's my time. Imagine speaking as the other woman. I would start off by saying, "I may be many things, but a home-wrecker is not one of them." Whenever there is a situation between a man and a woman, in most cases the woman gets the bad name. Here is where I am with that: all narrow-minded people can kiss my ass, like her husband has been doing. Right now, it's time for me to hypothetically tell my side of the story.

I am a very attractive, married woman. I go about my day and business trying to live life to the fullest however it's dealt to me. Throughout my life men have come at me—mostly men who belong to other women. They tend to offer me things, take me places, pay for me to meet them out of town, and whatever it takes for them to lie with me. This has not always been my thing, but like the wife, I've been in the shoes of my husband taking me through bullshit.

We've had our fights and disappointing moments. His lying, cheating, and not holding up to his part in the marriage. Broke as fuck. Always promising shit. I have this thing that I am not afraid to let a man know how I feel. Some may say I'm aggressive.

However, the last straw was one evening when my husband and I were sitting in the kitchen and the doorbell rang. We were not on the best of terms. Bills due and my feeling overwhelmed, knowing that I was the breadwinner. We had also been dealing with his bitch consistently calling our house and hanging up, calling me names and asking me, "Do you know where your man is right now?" She even went so far as to send me a photo of him asleep in her bed. Apparently, he had fallen asleep at her house. Men are so fucking stupid and trusting with these women. He had no idea what she was doing. Both he and she were only thinking about the "p." Him, "pussy," and her, getting "paid."

Of course she sent me the photo. I was hurt beyond any imagination. I had been anticipating leaving him. Definitely for a Prince Charming, sugar daddy, hoodlum, or preacher. Anybody who could whisk me away from this bullshit.

But back to the doorbell ringing. It was her. His side bitch. I answered the door, and there she was, standing with a newborn in a car seat. This hoe pushed past me into my house. Times past, she had described to me on the phone during one of our arguments how my home looked. This woman had been in my house with my husband before.

What do you think? Does it sound like he had her in my house? Was I wrong?

Anyway, by the time my husband made his way up to where we were, we were going at it. I could not believe what was happening. This was some Lifetime shit.

After sitting the baby down, she turned around and started swinging at me. She was yelling, "Take this bastard baby. Your son is now going to live with you and this fake bitch. You messed up my life, and now you want to quit me? You want to go on living in holy matrimony with her? Not happening."

This girl had to be no more than twenty—twenty-five on a good day. We tussled and rolled around. My husband tried to break it up. Luckily one of my older kids was there and called the police. Finally, he broke us apart with the help of my oldest. I was bleeding. This heifer had scratched me. We both had torn clothes. She smelled like weed.

CPD at the door, and chaos for days. The night ended with her in handcuffs. My husband spent the night trying to explain. We were left with a newborn. His newborn. He was trying not to claim it. After going through channels, this turned out to be extremely rough on our relationship.

Several months went by. It was confirmed that it was his child. I had to accept the baby in order to continue with my husband. I did. Bittersweet. He was doing everything he could to make it right. A part of my heart went out of the door the minute his baby mama pushed into our house. By the way, she got community service. She refused to take the baby back. My husband, as wrong as this situation was, did not want to see his child grow up in a foster home. I had grown attached to the child over the several months we were trying to figure everything out. I knew in my heart that the child was innocent and should not be punished for what the adults controlling his life were doing. Yes, it was a boy. Although I had accepted this challenge to work with my husband to raise his child, it did not take away the emptiness I was feeling inside toward my husband. I had to choose to move on. But deep down inside, I had not forgotten or forgiven him for the trauma he had put our family through.

I had grown a cold heart toward women and men. How could another woman do this, knowing this would hurt another human-being? Another woman. As for men, they deserved whatever they had coming.

With all of that being said, this brings me back to why I couldn't give a damn about another person, male or female. Now, everything was all about me and what made me happy. If I wanted to entertain some extracurricular activity, then I did. I think sometimes my husband had a strong clue that I was messing around, and rather than bringing it up and going toe-to-toe about the topic of cheating, he just let it go.

The most exciting affair was the one with the bougie bitch's husband. He was easy prey. I knew he was attracted to me when he saw me. I knew this because of how strongly he was flirting. His wife thought that she was all that and a bag of cherries. Just the thought of taking something from her gave me gratitude. I know she probably had wronged a woman or two in her lifetime by the way I saw some of the guys hit on her when ole boy was not around. For some strange notion, she reminded me of my husband's baby mama. At least her looks, body type, and height. However, my husband's baby mama was ghetto. Ole boy's wife was prissy and stuck up.

At the end of the day, we connected. Her man was spending a lot of his spare time with me. When I would ask, "Where is your wife?" He said probably at the mall. Leaving her man unattended was great for me.

I took the liberty to invite him to meet me at our hide-out hotel. Of course, he didn't refuse. We rolled around for a while and began to chat afterward. He invited me to meet him out of town. Of course, all expenses paid. He traveled quite a bit. His wife never accompanied him. She was too busy doing her own thing. Leaving it up to me to babysit. I was up for the challenge, seeing that my home life was not a fairy tale. Newborn at home whom I had grown to adore, a husband who could bore the shit out of a dead person, and the four walls of a house that was not like the one my sugar daddy had.

I started to fall for this guy. He was charming, dressed nicely, was very well groomed, intelligent, deliberate, and direct but not rude. One thing: he would not engage in too much conversation about his wife. I would on occasion ask questions. He would turn it off by saying "Do you really want to waste time talking about that or them?" He subtly was letting me know that his married life was off-limits. I asked him if he would consider leaving her. Funnily enough, he appeared cool when he answered. To think about it, he actually did not answer at that moment. He showed me by not hitting me up for a week after that. We would talk once a day or at least once every other day. That made me feel kind of cheap. He kicked me down and gave me money for a down payment on my car (he lightweight took care of me, paying a few minor bills), but she was off-limits.

The more time I spent with him, the more my feelings grew. I started to become very envious of them as a couple when I saw them at events. Her walking around like she didn't have a care in the world.

On the other hand, besides what he did for me, my husband and I were struggling. With the relationship, finances, and simply just being together. Since the infidelity of my husband, I had evened the score several times over with various affairs. However, this one was a challenge. He cared about me as long as I did not cross the line. His reputation, wife, and public affection were unsaid but made clear through his actions they were off-limits whenever those subjects came up.

I think several people in the organization wondered about us. I know his wife suspected because every chance I got I subtly let her ass know. Yes, your man is fucking me. Interestingly enough, after so many years of the back-and-forth, she started to be over me and my shenanigans. It was as if her mind were somewhere else and she had a little something something going on herself. However, that did not work in my favor. I would have thought it would. The more she seemed to pull away from him, he pulled away from me.

One particular event we were all attending, she appeared to be preoccupied with this one couple. Jesus! The guy was fine as hell, but he was with someone. My lover, her husband, appeared to be annoyed and running behind her. I was pissed. Then he had the audacity to dance with her. I really felt some kind of way. I thought he was really feeling me. I had been with him several years, in the cut. But... that's where he was keeping me. In the cut. I had no right because I was married.

My affections and feelings had grown. I was in love with this man and thought he loved me, but I found he actually loved his wife. It started off with my getting a little revenge, punishing a bougie bitch and enjoying a little wining and dining for a change. Feelings were not supposed to happen. He was starting to be unavailable, distant, and basically communication had ceased. He was probably chasing her. He told me that things at work had gotten busy and he didn't know how much time he would have anymore. Was this arrogant motherfucker breaking up with me? Was he trying to make his home life better, or had he found another to do his dirt with? I felt used and thrown away.

My thought was that I was going to confront his wife. At the end of the day, what did I have to lose other than a washed-up marriage of my own? Maybe if she left him, he and I could move forward. I guess I should have thought about everything before making a move. That could have made him hate me for wrecking his home. Hell, a bitch wrecked mine. It looked like to me it was already challenged. He wouldn't have been messing with me in the first place if it were all that. Like I said in the beginning, I got to shop just as much as she. He had taken care of me and paid me to sit on the sideline. Well, I no longer wanted to be benched. Game on. He needed to tell me who he wanted. Because I would tell.

Chapter 9.

BACK THE FUCK UP: IT'S OVER

As the husband, I'm dealing with my side chick threatening me. I guess the bitch was serious because ole girl hit me up, talking a lot of bullshit.

What kills me is that in the beginning, they were willing to go along with any and everything. They allow you to wine and dine them. They don't refuse cash, if we are offering. They were the perfect person. Dressed nice, smelled nice, and on their best behavior. Sexy, confident, and high maintenance but self-maintained. Was willing to do things in the bedroom that a therapist couldn't explain. They were always available. Creative, thoughtful, and magical was the relationship. Very spontaneous.

As time went by, all that shit started to change. Trying to be careful, I had a conversation up front on what it was. Somewhere between stating, "This is fun," and, "I still love my wife," her ass stopped listening and started filling in the blanks with how she wanted the story to go. This is what I do and have done in all of my relationships. Now in this one.

I had always kept a spare. The spare had always played her position and not caused me any issues. I tended to be able to sense when they were getting too caught up. I truly understood what the other man was saying in chapter 6 about when the women act stupid, causing us to start the deactivator plan. *Back the fuck up*! I've rocked with this one for several years. Actually, truth be told, she was feeling me far before my wife even paid attention to what was going on.

Back to the conversation. She called me, going off about how I had disrespected her at the event. I had started to be distant. Here was where the shit hit the fan. She got beside herself and said that she was not going to tolerate it. She was two steps from telling my wife about us. First of all this bitch had lost her mind. I had to let her know. What was she going to do after that? This Bitch had one shot at my wife. That was her last and only card. What was she going to do when my wife told her she didn't give a fuck? She knew about my affairs and supported them. We had an open relationship. But I wanted to know how my side chics husband was going to handle me rolling around with her stank ass for some years.

Believe it or not, this had happened with another young lady I dealt with some years ago, threatening to tell my girl. The line that my girl and I had an open relationship worked back then. I figured I would bluff again. The problem with this one, to my surprise, was she and her husband actually did have an open relationship. In order for them to continue after the out-of-wedlock baby, he agreed for them to open up the relationship and remain married and friends until possibly they could rekindle what they had, if at all for the sake of the kids. At least this was the BS she fed me. She proceeded to read me my rights. Asking me if I loved her, and I did not. I still loved my wife. She told me that I wasn't shit and that I needed to be honest with her. She also said that my wife was a fool and that she didn't know who I was. A no-good piece of shit who treated women like objects.

Like I said to her, "I'm not quite understanding the hostile behavior. We both went into this with no expectations, rules, or inhibitions (Sound familiar?). You told me you didn't care about her or my situation. Everything was cool. We are feeling each other so let's do it. What's up? What I do with my wife is now a problem? To answer your question, I care about you, but I still love my wife. This was never to go past fun, friendship, and a fuck."

She started crying and saying that I had used her. She kept repeating, "What would your wife say?"

Truth be told about my wife, of course she suspected this woman but was not into that superfly bullshit mentioned earlier. This would definitely destroy my marriage. I had to let this bitch down easy. She actually had nothing to lose, not even a care in the world about losing her husband.

It would be a long day and day from hell when I learned that my wife happened to be home listening to everything I said.

I finally just told my side bitch, it was what it was. Move the fuck on. If she ever needed anything, I would be there for her, but as far as this relationship, it's over.

After the phone call, I headed up to change my clothes before my wife got in. As I walked up the stairs, I discovered the bedroom light was on and the door was open. Fuck, she was home!

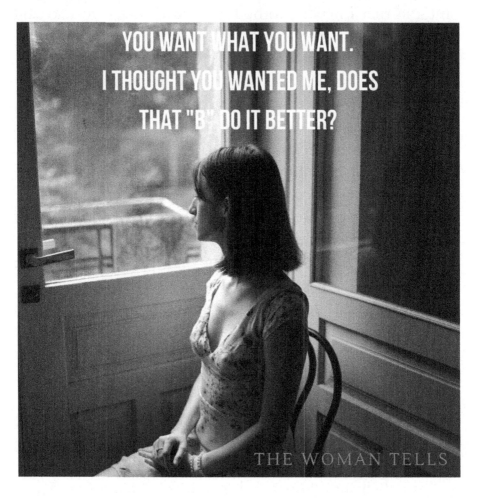

YOU WANT WHAT YOU WANT.
I THOUGHT YOU WANTED ME, DOES
THAT "B" DO IT BETTER?

THE WOMAN TELLS

Chapter 10.

MY SURPRISE, MY SECRET

Moving back in time to the scenario that happened on the yacht the night the thot was invited on. This was a very tough evening for me.

As I mentioned, a thot on the yacht pitching, our not being in a good place, and my not feeling my best made for a rough day. However, while driving to the emergency room, cramps were getting unbearable. Before leaving the boat, I had put on something for protection. I'm always prepared. I had started to bleed during intercourse. Something that had never happened to me. I have always been exceptionally neat and on top of my game with my girl, hygiene, etc....He noticed the blood and made it an ordeal. OCD MF.

I arrived at the emergency room. Thank God it was relatively empty. My pad was soaked with an unusual amount of blood. I had started bleeding and cramping really heavily. They immediately took me in. I spent the next four hours there. There I learned that I had miscarried.

The doctor asked if I knew that I was pregnant. I started bawling uncontrollably. He apologized and continued working on me. They wanted to keep me overnight for observation, but I insisted that I needed to go. I promised the doctor I was going straight home. He released me to two friends. One to drive my car.

I never called ole boy to tell him. I didn't know if I would tell him at all. What would he say? God was on my side. My husband happened to be gone.

I stayed in bed the next day and a half. I spoke with Dude several times those days. He would FaceTime me to see what I was up to. He would always ask, "What did you eat?" He would laugh and talk awhile, then off he went with what and whomever he was with. He never knew. I told him I was lying down because I was tired. I was sure a serious conversation would follow later—or maybe not. Some things are better left where they are.

I was very emotional afterward. I felt even more attached to him. I was very sad that I lost his child. I guess all things worked out, considering the circumstances. What would have happened had that come into play? There's no doubt some things would have been an automatic decision.

Nevertheless, the place I was in now, I had a lot to sort out. My husband mentioned he wanted to talk when he got home. He had been trying to show me more attention. He had been making plans and arrangements for things. This was something I wanted for a long time. I guess you can want something so badly, and when it does not happen, you move on. Emotionally I've moved on from that. I figured it would all work out because I had become very numb to both. Life was taking a turn for me. Right now I wanted to do me and only me. Whatever that looked like. Now I had something that I needed to speak to him about as well.

It sounded like I heard him come in. So I decided to walk downstairs to greet him.

As I was walking down the hall, I could hear him on the phone arguing with someone. As I got closer, I could tell who it was. My husband did not know that I was home. I stopped in the hall and listened to the entire conversation. One thing's for sure: my curiosity was satisfied. It was no question about who the other woman was. It was whom I had suspected. I guess I blamed him for taking recess, kicking all the shit off. At that very moment, I had to make a decision on what I needed to do.

I walked back to the room and turned on the TV. He got off the call. He was definitely shocked to learn that I was home. I know as he walked up the stairs to our room, seeing the light and TV on startled him. It must have been the walk to Hell. His mind wondering, "Did she hear me? Was I loud? Was the TV on the entire time and I missed it?" What a web we weave.

His first words were, "Hey, you, how was your day?"

I answered, "All you do is lie. I heard you talking to her."

He looked at me like he had seen a ghost. Then he said to me, "What in the fuck is that supposed to mean?"

I said, "Let me explain it in English."

He interrupted me. He went on to lie and say that he was talking to his admin about something she didn't get done at work. He went on and on about how I always think the worst in a situation. "You hear things that are not there. You are always focusing on the wrong shit."

He continued with the reverse psychology tactics until I said, "Please stop with the bullshit. I know who you were talking to because you called her name while talking. Apparently, to get her attention because she was going off so bad. You also called her Babe, might I add. Since when did you start to call your admin Babe? If that is a practice, that's a serious human resource issue that you can have trouble with. My suggestion would be to stop. However, I doubt very seriously you are calling your admin Babe. Remember, I was your admin at one point. Regardless of how attracted you were to me, you remained professional at all times. I think you have some things to sort out. In the meantime, I think we should separate. I'm moving out!"

The Woman Tells

Chapter 11.

HIS SURPRISE, HIS SECRET

In life, sometimes the outcome can take a twist that you did not plan for. He called me to talk. The news was shocking. I found out his secret. I was not surprised in the least. Hurt, confused, perplexed, and mystified, but not surprised.

His actions had become distant and dismissive, but in the same breath, he was always speaking about how he wanted us to plan a future together. His words were that he loved me ever since I came into his life. Everything had changed. He had changed. He said that I was embedded in his heart and soul. All he had done was plan his future as if I would be with him. No other woman had measured up. He went on to say that in the midst of his lonely time, he had started spending time with Alice again, and now if I didn't see a future with him, he would make it work with her.

I really don't think this motherfucker knew who and what he wanted. Me being me. I am a strong Cherokee Indian and half-black woman. Both sides can catch most bullshit any man dishes out. I can serve it up and send it right back.

To his surprise, I asked what happened to the thot on the yacht. I proceeded to let him know that one of my friends had seen him out with a pregnant woman. He tried to skate around his answer, but I knew. He decided to be transparent with me. Apparently, he tested and it turned out the baby was not his. I guess their fling had run its course and trouble. It was probably the reasoning for his hitting up his lifetime standby Alice.

I thought it best not to bring up the miscarriage. My motto was, "Go be all you can be with whomever you can be that with. If another is making you happy and they fit your program—as you like it, intelligent and whatever else—however you build out your model is great. Go for it. I'm not for everybody and everybody is not for me."

He was shocked at how calm and accepting I was to his news. He was not telling me that he wanted her, but if I could not commit 100% to him, then he wanted to give someone else a shot. I agreed, as I should. He really was not expecting that outcome. He was used to breaking up with women and having them chase him. He then would move them to the "friend" category.

I know this from reading something the Russian witch bitch wrote on social media. Dumbass! One of his idiots. She would always write about them, ending with ridiculous hashtags like "my best friend," and "my normal." Bitch, that's only so he can keep you bottled up where he wants you. This left him open to see other people without you being able to legitimately complain. I said legitimately. Anybody can complain. He occasionally will take you out, play with you, get some pussy, and then put you back.

As for me, I'm not a friend zone kind of a bitch. One thing you are not going to do is send me to the island of hopefuls. Hoping that he comes back around to our team. If it was over, that was what it was. One and done. For one, it was what it was, and if God saw it differently and we found our way back, then so be it.

He continued to try to assure me that it was a mistake and that I was who he wanted. He was prepared to give me what I needed.

I told him, "At this point I'm not sure what it is that I need. Definitely not a relationship with a person who's not honest. Not to me or to her or them."

When you look at it, everyone in this story was being dishonest regardless of how they got there. He wanted us both to take some time to think about what we really wanted. I was quite aware of what it was I wanted. I did not tell him that my husband and I had separated, as it had happened several months prior. With no return in sight. I wanted to watch his behavior without tainted knowledge that I was free. If he did not have it in him to continue to treat me like I wanted to be treated or love me without an expectation or plan, unconditionally, then he was not for me either.

I had made a lot of bad decisions and mistakes over the years. Some I would take back, and some I would do over and over again. Which one(s) will totally remain with me.

I told him for right now until I can figure myself out, let's break! It appears that I was complicating things for him. We both knew in our hearts that we were and will always be soul mates. We both said it. We had both gone somewhere where we had not been in our feelings. It was clear that no one else could take us there. We both shared that we were still in love but had a lot of shit to figure out and take care of. We made love like we had never before. We parted that day, with no end in mind, but with hope for the future. Neither could say the words. Just with thoughts that it was going to work itself out.

Which side is greener? My side or her side of the bed?

@thewomantells

Chapter 12.

ACCOUNTABILITY

Once again, life is all about what you make it. Goals and dreams can come true. However, back to the first paragraph of this novel, you have to be willing to see it through. Not quit when you are almost to the finish line. Get nervous and work another half-cocked plan with someone you decided to settle for or make it work. Somewhere down the line, the insufficiencies are going to surface, and you will be back to square A.

In this story, doors were opened, some closed, some unlocked, waiting to open or close, and some open, still waiting on what's to come. Some relationships are made in heaven. Some generated from nothing and are just meant to be. Meant to be does not necessarily mean forever but for a season to teach a lesson. To help us grow and find our way. Not every relationship will work out exactly how you envisioned it. Some things will. Like each character in this novel, you have a choice to choose how you will handle your situation. Be it with patience, revenge, prayer, walking away, or staying. It's your choice.

Everyone in a relationship has a role and contributes to the outcome. The best advice is to make sure you own your piece in the scenario. Take accountability for what you did and did not do in the relationship. Make sure it's the best it can be.

Also, make sure the expectations you have for your partner are ones that you are following as well. Keep it 100%. Communicate your concerns to your partner. As you can see, it's very easy for another to enter in through a loophole, causing what could result in a destructive end, separation, time apart from your partner, or he or she finds another love that results in their ever after. Be it mentally or physically, it separates you.

People change, and that's a fact. However, usually if both parties in the relationship are being fulfilled, you leave little room for another to slither in. If you have grown to a place that you feel your partner or spouse has not gotten successfully with you, then it is your responsibility to share that with them. You are not required to be somewhere that's not making you happy.

Back to the statistics. A relationship only has a slim chance and odds to make it as it is. No additives are needed. No matter how it started off. Follow your heart. Life is too short. Misery and settling should not be an option. Happiness comes in many forms. Which brand do you want? As a woman I will tell you, I'm not sure about you, but I choose love however it shows up.

Follow Karla on Social Media

The Woman Tells

Website: www.thewomantells.com
IG: @thewomantells.com
Email: slay@shopkarlasklozet.com
Facebook: The Woman Tells

Karla's Klozet Online Retail & Consignment Shop

Website: www.shopkarlasklozet.com
Email: slay@shopkarlasklozet.com
IG: @shopkarlasklozet
Facebook: Karla's Klozet
Blog: **www.shopkarlasklozet**
Blog/Wordpress: **www.kkztblog.com**

Building A Circle of Friends, LLC

Website: www.bacof.org
Email: info@bacof.org
IG: @bacoforg
Facebook: Building A Circle of Friends
CLUBHOUSE: Karla Davis-Luster

The Woman Tells

JOURNAL

Tell Your Story

The Woman Tells Journal is a tool to record notes on your behaviors, times, dates, special moments, positive circumstances or areas needing work. These are areas that you personally have control over that occur in the relationship. The information can be used to create an action plan to work on improving ones self. "Self Reflection" is always a great way to hopefully establish a better outcome. You should always ask yourself, "What could I have done better to help improve, change or make a decision regarding my scenario?"

The Woman Tells · JOURNAL

"What's yours is ours and what's mine is theirs."

The Woman Tells · JOURNAL

"P…y or Pride?
Which one do you like?? I'm accommodating."

The Woman Tells · JOURNAL

"Statistically speaking, he's mine.
Your stats must be wrong."

The Woman Tells · JOURNAL

"You want what you want.
I thought you wanted me, does that "B" do it better."

The Woman Tells · JOURNAL

"I am who I am. Self-satisfaction is a preference
no matter the outcome!"

June

"Who is that creeping in my window?
I don't care, my alarm is on."

July

"Have you been watering my man properly?
Perhaps you can make him grow."

The Woman Tells · JOURNAL

August

"I like mustard on my hotdog,
but that condiment is out of stock."

September

"How do you define happiness?
I thought it was me."

October

"Lover, Liar or Lust …
which one are you in the relationship."

November

"Life in the dark,
can somebody turn on the lights?????"

November

The Woman Tells · JOURNAL

"Which side is greener?
My side or her side of the bed?"

Made in the USA
Monee, IL
07 August 2021